CUT-HAND
the
MOUNTAIN
MAN

CUT-HAND the MOUNTAIN MAN

by

Joseph Millard

CHILTON BOOKS

A DIVISION OF CHILTON COMPANY
PUBLISHERS
PHILADELPHIA AND NEW YORK

For my son, Michael, who supplied

the title and applied the spur

CUT-HAND
the
MOUNTAIN
MAN

I

YOUNG Dick Wootton awoke suddenly in the misty blackness, his nerves tingling with a sharp sense of alarm. From somewhere close by came the pound of running feet on planking and the urgent shouting of many voices.

Instinctively, Dick threw back his blanket, snatched his long rifle cradled against his body and started to spring to his feet. Something smashed against his bare head with stunning force. He fell back dazed, his ears ringing and his vision filled with bursting many-colored lights. He shook his head to clear it and suddenly he remembered where he was and realized what had happened. For a moment he felt almighty foolish.

He was on board the stern-wheel steamer *Yellowstone,* nearing the end of its four-hundred-fifty-mile run up the Missouri River to Independence, the last outpost of civilization in that spring of 1836. He had been sleeping on the afterdeck, rolled up in his blanket under a big Conestoga wagon. When he was awakened so abruptly and started to lunge to his feet, he had slammed his head against the underside of the oak wagon bed.

"It like to've knocked my fool brains out," Dick muttered disgustedly, gingerly fingering the lump swelling up under his brown hair.

The tumult that had awakened him was still going on somewhere forward. Ducking cautiously, he scrambled out from under the wagon and stood up. A gusty wind drove a fine, chill drizzle of rain against his face. The swampy smell of the river was dank and heavy in his nostrils. He could hear the roar of the rain-swollen torrent above the pound of the engines and the threshing of paddles at the stern. Above the stacks the mist glowed with the lurid reflection of the fires below. Twin plumes of sparks gushed back as sweating firemen hurled chunks of hardwood into the furnace.

All around him the deck was jammed with loaded wagons of every size and kind, ranked hub to hub and lashed down, their wheels blocked by chunks of timber. Dick threaded his way between them to the narrow walkway along the guardrail and ran toward the bow.

He came around the high square tower of the pilothouse onto a scene of feverish excitement. All the men on board were crowded into the bow. There were trappers in greasy buckskins, traders and merchants in fine broadcloth, freighters in heavy jeans, and westering emigrants in homespun, jostling and craning to look ahead. Blazing torches of pitch pine, lashed to the rails and the corners of the pilothouse, lit the deck and the oily, heaving waters beyond.

A knot of men had climbed onto a wagon for a better view and Dick clambered up on the wheel beside them. From here he could see over the crowd to the bow where two roustabouts of the steamboat crew were crouching beyond the rail, each poising an ash pole at least fifteen feet in length.

"What's going on?" Dick asked. "Is something wrong?"

"Plenty," a man on the wagon said grimly. "The river undercut the bank somewhere upstream and dumped a full acre or more of forest into the flood. It's coming down on us in huge chunks solid enough to crush this tub like an eggshell if we hit it head on." His voice went tight and shrill. "There comes another one now."

Peering ahead, Dick saw the shadowy bulk of what appeared to be a small island with two or three good-sized trees rising from a dense tangle of underbrush. Then he realized that it *was* an island, but one afloat on the raging torrent. It was dead ahead and bearing straight down on the *Yellowstone* with awesome, relentless majesty, bobbing ponderously on the flood.

Its front was studded with big rocks caught in a tangle of tree roots, rocks massive enough to shatter the steamer's bow. Worse, a solid impact could send the trees crashing down onto the deck and the row of cubbyhole cabins where the women and children were quartered.

A chorus of shouts went up. "Veer off, Cap'n! Veer off! They'll never be able to turn that chunk out of our way, pushing with those toothpicks."

The captain leaned from the pilothouse window, almost over Dick's head, to bawl back, "We can't veer off. We're between two swirling eddies full of rocks and snags. If we were to swing out of the current either way, we'd be sucked into a whirlpool and our bottom ripped out. Our only chance is to fend it off and hold course."

The oncoming mass was more clearly visible now, its vast bulk dwarfing the little steamboat. Dick's breath caught as he visualized the futility of pitting human muscles and two slender poles against that irresistible force. It looked as though the first big adventure of his twenty years was also to be his last. With the raging river swollen far beyond its banks, there was little hope of anyone surviving long enough to reach solid ground.

His thoughts flashed to his parents, awaiting his return to the family tobacco plantation in Christian County, Kentucky. There was little chance that they would ever learn his fate. As far as they knew he was still somewhere along the Natchez Trace, walking home from a year's stay on his uncle's cotton plantation in Mississippi. He had not written them of his sudden decision to turn west for one quick look at St. Louis and the frontier before settling down to the dull routine of farming. After all, he had expected the detour to take only a few days and there was no set time for his arrival at home.

If his parents worried, it would not be about Dick's ability to take care of himself on the perilous five-hundred-mile Trace. At twenty he was man-grown and bull-strong with a stocky, powerful frame. He was a crack rifle shot and skilled woodsman. When he was a small child, playing with a sharp ax had cost

3

him the last two fingers of his left hand. The loss had never interfered with his riding, shooting, or fighting but it marked him with a brand he would carry to his grave.

His reverie was interrupted by another burst of shouting. "It's swinging aside! We're saved!"

The great mass, drifting too close to the edge of the channel, had been caught by the whirling currents of the eddy and was being slowly but surely drawn aside. For a moment it appeared that the danger of collision was past.

Then the shouts turned to groans. As the front of the floating island was pulled into the whirlpool, a long tail of tangled roots and driftwood logs was being swung directly into the *Yellowstone's* path. Anxious voices yelled, "Back water, Cap'n. Hold back and give it time to pull clear."

"I dassn't," the captain bawled back. "We're barely holding our own against the current now. If we lose any more headway we'll be sucked right into the eddy for sure."

The distance between dwindled to rods, to yards, then to scant feet. The two roustabouts at the bow went up on their toes and drove the ends of their poles hard against the looming bulk. Bent forward, shoving with all their strength, they fought the irresistible force that drove them backward, their calked boots gouging raw furrows in the deck.

With a roar, the whole crowd of watchers surged forward to grab the poles and add their strength to the mighty effort. Dick propped his rifle against the wagon seat, sprang down, and rammed his way into the crowd. He glimpsed the rounded butt of a pole and drove his powerful shoulder against it, his feet clawing the deck planks for leverage. He met the relentless push and fought it with every ounce of strength in his big-boned frame. His muscles creaked with the strain. He was blinded by perspiration streaming into his eyes and deafened by the pound of his own blood in his ears.

For a long moment the thrust drove him backward. Then it was easing, and suddenly he found himself inching ahead as the momentum of the looming mass yielded sullenly to their efforts. A man's voice shouted, "That's enough. Ease off on the poles. We're going to clear."

Dick fell back, panting, and dashed the sweat from his eyes. The huge bulk of the floating island was sliding past the steamboat on the starboard side, so close a man could step across to it from the rail. A loud rasping sound rose above the pound of the walking beam as protruding roots scraped along the hull.

Then the noise ceased and the gap of black water widened as the sturdy little steamer surged ahead into the clear. Everyone yelled wildly. Men pounded one another on the back and shouted their relief while overhead the whistle let go a thin, triumphant tooting.

Looking around, Dick was surprised to discover that the whole broad surface of the swollen river was now visible, dotted with patches of boiling white foam and dark masses of debris. The rain had stopped and dawn was breaking in a riot of pink and cream that filled the eastern sky. With daylight the pilot would be able to see any other drifting masses far enough ahead to select a clear channel. The danger of collision was over.

The captain leaned from the pilothouse window and cupped his hands to his mouth. "You gents'll be pleased to know we'll make Independence Landing before noon today. Three and a half days from St. Louis is mighty good time, considering the high water we've had to buck."

Dick Wootton's voice joined the cheer that went up. In a few short hours he would actually be in the most talked-of town in the United States, the last outpost of civilization on the threshold of the Wilderness West.

2

In MIDMORNING Dick Wootton stood with the crowd at the forward rail, all straining eagerly ahead for their first look at fabled Independence. He was packed and ready to go ashore. His few personal belongings were rolled in the blanket strapped on his back. His powder horn was slung from his shoulder, bullet pouch and cap box at his belt. One hand held tightly to the fine new breech-loading percussion-cap Hall rifle that had cost him a sizable chunk of his year's wages.

Staring out across the broad roiling brown flood, Dick murmured, "The Missouri's an almighty big river."

A whiskered emigrant beside him snorted. "Don't call that hog wallow a river, son. A river's got *water* in it. This'n is nothing but mud soup, too thick to drink and too thin to plow."

A gaunt trapper in greasy buckskins gave them a mischievous grin. "You gents ought to see her a month from now, when the rains stop. This here valley dries up so the only way a steamboat can get through is to send a boy ahead with a sprinkling pot to wet down the dust."

Dick joined the laughter, then broke off, his eyes widening. Coming down the river, spinning and bobbing on the flood, was a strange object that resembled a huge brown ball. Pointing, he gasped, "What on earth is that?"

The trapper squinted. "A buffler, son, drowned and swole up like a p'isoned pup."

Dick felt a tingle of excitement. His first sight of a buffalo, even as a dead and bloated carcass, was indisputable proof that he had reached the edge of the Western wilderness. Beyond lay

6

a million square miles of mountain and desert, rimmed by hostile Mexico on the south and west and equally hostile Britain on the north.

"Which way you headed?" the emigrant asked. "Oregon, Californy, or down to Santa Fe for trade?"

"None of 'em," Dick said regretfully. "When the *Yellowstone* turns downriver tomorrow, I'll be on it heading home to Kentucky. That's where I was bound, up the Natchez Trace, when I got such a hankering just to see the West that I turned off at Nashville. I only figured to have a look at St. Louis, but when I found out I could take deck passage to Independence for only four dollars each way, I grabbed the chance." He swallowed a knot in his throat. "I'd give an arm to go on, but Pa wants me to settle down and take over the plantation."

The emigrant eyed him with new respect. "You walked up the Natchez Trace by yourself? That's a mighty risky trip, I hear. Didn't you meet none of them bloodthirsty land pirates that're killing and robbing travelers there?"

"Likely I did," Dick said. "I met some mighty rough characters I wouldn't trust behind my back, and some mighty slick ones I wouldn't trust either, but they didn't bother me. I guess they figured I wasn't worth robbing."

"Hmm!" The trapper turned and eyed Dick's stocky figure. "I'd say it's more like they didn't figure it'd pay to tangle with a set of shoulders like yourn."

The talk was interrupted by the long-drawn hoot of the steamer's whistle, flinging the news of their coming out across the sodden prairie. The captain shouted, "Independence Landing. Everybody get set to go ashore."

Dick stared in bewilderment as the little stern-wheeler curved in toward the landing. He had visualized a roaring boomtown, as busy and crowded as St. Louis. But all he could see was a clump of straggling willows, a couple of weatherbeaten shanties, and a mountainous pile of cordwood for the steamboats. The trapper saw his expression and chuckled.

"This here's only Independence Landing, son. Independence proper is six miles inland, up that road you see beyond."

The gangplank squealed out and Dick was swept ashore in the surging rush. A few people set off up the muddy road on foot but the majority were waiting for their teams to be led up from belowdecks and the wagons unloaded. Dick set out with the hikers.

The soaked earth steamed under a blazing sun. As far as he could see the rolling prairie was green with new grass and flecked with the bright colors of early wild flowers. Meadowlarks sang and overhead a hawk wheeled lazily in a brassy sky. Where the river began its northward curve into the great unknown a row of giant cottonwood trees shimmered in the sun. It was all new and strange and fiercely exciting to Dick Wootton and he ached at the thought of turning back from the very threshold of adventure.

Suddenly he crested a long rise and met the vanguard of the crowd rushing down from Independence to meet the steamboat. Merchants and traders pounded by on fine horses, racing for first chance at the dollars in the emigrants' pockets. Behind them came empty freight wagons on their way to pick up loads of supplies from St. Louis and the East. Mule teams trotted by with harness jingling and traces looped up, ready to be hooked onto wagons. They were followed by crowds on foot, hurrying to meet friends and families, to sell something or steer newcomers to a particular shop.

Dick had never seen such a solid tide of traffic. Yet it was no more than a pale preview of coming years, when the town would be forced to pave this road with the first macadam west of the Mississippi.

From the top of a prairie swell he looked down at last on Independence, the jumping-off place for the Wilderness West. The nine-year-old village clustered around the neat, square Jackson County courthouse, a huddle of shanties, shacks, and tents, with here and there a house of substantial brick. This, in turn, was hemmed in by a vast sprawling circle of corrals, camps, and wagon parks. Here was the emigrants' last chance to refit, repair, and stock up for the journey west and the whole town was noisily dedicated to selling them everything they needed.

Dick passed an emigrant camp, alive with yelling children and barking dogs. Several wagons were jacked up, their axles glistening with bear grease. Others stood with gaunt, arching ribs bare, awaiting new canvas tops, double layers of finest Osnaberg sheeting to turn back rain and the burning sun.

Men hunkered by a fire, hammering a three-inch iron tire onto a wagon wheel. From every direction the air quivered to the crash and clang of blacksmiths' hammers. A roped-off lot was piled high with fly-covered buffalo hides and bales of beaver pelts awaiting shipment to St. Louis. Dick hurried on, gagging at the fearful stench.

He passed a train of freighters loading for the journey down to Santa Fe, in Mexico. The massive wagons, each capable of hauling five tons, were piled high with hardware and cotton goods for the rugged eight-hundred-mile journey. Coming back, they would bring that scarcest of frontier commodities, hard money, huge Mexican silver dollars to be cut into halves, quarters, and bits for small change.

In the town itself, Dick trudged past Colonel Smallwood Nolan's tavern, the westernmost hotel in America, with accommodations of a sort for four hundred guests. The muddy street was lined with outfitting stores, one operated by the sons of Daniel Boone, another by Lillburn Boggs, future governor of Missouri. Still another was run by Sam Owens, whose half sister Mary was at that moment visiting back in Illinois and being shyly courted by a gangling country lawyer named Abraham Lincoln.

Dick wandered on in a daze of pounding excitement, jostled by throngs of teamsters, mountain men, dark-skinned Mexicans, peddlers, and Indians in dirty blankets. Here and there, grim figures in somber black stalked through the crowd, ignoring mutters of hatred. These were "Mormonites" who believed Independence stood on the site of the Garden of Eden and had settled there to await Judgment Day.

A shanty, larger than its neighbors, bore a crude sign: Bent & St. Vrain. As Dick came abreast, a very tall, thin man ran out the door to hail him. "You looking for a job, son?"

Dick stopped short. "What kind of job?"

"We've a freight train pulling out in the morning for Bent's Fort, on the Arkansas, and we're shy a teamster. Can you handle mules?"

"That," Dick said dryly, "is a point me and mules haven't settled between us yet."

The thin man laughed and slapped his shoulder. "You'll do. I like a feller who doesn't brag on how good he is." He eyed Dick anxiously. "How about it? Twenty a month and the best grub on the trail. No fear of Injuns, either. We travel to the Arkansas with a big Santa Fe train—fifty-seven wagons and every man a crack shot. Redskins are too smart to attack an outfit that sizable."

Dick drew a deep breath. The plantation could get along without him another month. "I'll take it."

"Good lad! Now what name do I put down for you?"

"Richens Lacy Wootton, but everybody calls me Dick."

"They better," the thin man said grimly. "If you stopped to whup every smart aleck who called you 'Lacy Pants' we'd never get to the fort. Now come in while I fit you out with necessaries. Those duds of yourn wouldn't last a week on the trail."

When Dick emerged he was indistinguishable from scores of teamsters on the street. He wore a blue cotton shirt and jeans, protected by "savers," stout leggings that tied above the knee. Cowhide boots and a flat, broad-brimmed Guayaquil hat completed his attire. At his hip hung a ten-inch Green River knife and tucked in his belt was a "Pup," a .40 caliber single-shot Kentucky pistol. Rolled under one arm was a red Mackinaw, a close-woven poncho that would be his bed and blanket at night. On cold or rainy days, he could poke his head through a slit in the center and be warmly covered from neck to heels.

Following directions, he found the seven Bent & St. Vrain wagons encamped in a grove of huge cottonwoods by a stream two miles west of town. They were already loaded and ready to roll, their cargoes of supplies and trade goods covered by tarpaulins. The mules, twelve to a wagon, were picketed close by, grazing on the tender new grass. The men lounged in the shade, mending harness or simply puffing their pipes and yarning.

The captain of the train, a lean, gray-eyed man named Osborn, sized Dick up as they shook hands and appeared to approve what he saw. He shouted introductions and the others crowded up with friendly greetings. All eyes were on his fine new Hall rifle and Dick proudly handed it over to be passed around for inspection. He noted that his was the only rifle using the new percussion caps. The others carried plain iron-bound flintlocks.

When Dick's rifle reached Osborn he examined it briefly and handed it back, his face expressionless. "A mighty handsome piece," he said, then added cryptically, "I hope you don't lose your hair over it."

Dick was puzzled and vaguely deflated but the captain turned away before he could ask questions. The men were clamoring for a demonstration and Dick knew that his own marksmanship as well as his rifle would be on trial. He grinned to himself, confident that neither would let him down.

A slanting gash was cut into the bark of a cottonwood and a white chip wedged in to serve as a target. Dick paced off a full two hundred yards and knelt to load. The other wagoners crowded close to watch but Osborn leaned against a tree off to one side, his face blank.

There was a murmur of surprise as Dick flipped up the movable breech to load, instead of pouring powder down the barrel as with the flintlocks. He took an oiled patch from the brass-covered chamber in the stock, wrapped it around a lead ball, and pushed it into place with his thumb. Closing the breech, he took a percussion cap from the box on his belt, fitting the tiny copper cup of fulminate over a cone-shaped nipple. The whole process took only seconds and he was ready to shoot.

Resting the end of his wiping stick on the ground, Dick laid the rifle barrel over his left wrist as a rest, took quick aim, and fired. The chip flew into the air in two pieces and a cheer went up.

"You can't beat a breechloader for speed," Dick said. "I can get off six shots a minute with this new Hall."

Osborn took a twig he was chewing out of his mouth and regarded it thoughtfully. "I've seen a buck Indian put ten arrows into the air in *half* a minute. If I were you, I'd figure on nailing him with my first shot, son."

"You saw my first shot," Dick said with some heat. "Are you saying it was an accident that I hit dead center?"

The captain straightened and his lips curved in a friendly smile. "I'm not belittling either your aim or your rifle, Dick. But out here that gun'll get you killed quick. There's nothin' Comanches like better than attacking in a driving rainstorm, when it's pitch-black and howling wet. Even if you can keep those caps dry enough to fire, how are you going to fit one over that tiny nipple in the dark, and how'll you keep a wind from blowing it right off before you can shoot? Or what do you do if you run out of caps back in the mountains?"

"I never thought of those points," Dick said, crestfallen. "I guess I better trade this fancy piece in for a flintlock. A fellow can always pick up a piece of flint on the ground, or at least a chip of rock that'll strike sparks."

Osborn gave Dick's shoulder a comforting squeeze. "That's a sound idea. There's no rifle pretty enough to be worth losing your hair over."

That afternoon Dick sadly traded his new Hall for a rugged Hawken Mountain Rifle, the right arm of the mountain men. A plain, sturdy, practical weapon of .50 caliber, it weighed twelve pounds and threw a half-ounce ball two hundred yards with accuracy. The compliments of his new comrades, and the fact that he could get off three shots a minute even with the clumsier muzzle-loading process helped offset his regrets at parting with the Hall.

Before rolling up in his new Mackinaw blanket, Dick wrote a short note to his parents. "I can make the one trip, collect good wages, and still be home in time for the tobacco-curing, so don't worry about me."

He fell asleep at last by the dying embers of the campfire, to dream of brave adventures in this exciting new world of the West. But not even Dick Wootton's wildest dreams that night could foresee the fantastic future that waited for him at the far end of the trail.

3

I⊤ WAS three in the morning when the racketing guns of the sentries aroused the camp for a new day. The sky still blazed with stars, the Big Dipper perched upended to the north, and the air was sharply chill. In the stillness, Dick could hear the sound of morning rifles from other camps and the high, thin wail of a bugle from one of the emigrant trains.

The men were rolling out, some grumpy and heavy-eyed with sleep, a few frisky and ready for horseplay. While fires were built up to light the camp, Dick joined the teamsters going to bring in their picketed mules. Luckily, he had had plenty of experience in handling the cantankerous jugheads back home, so he went at his job with calm assurance that brought a nod of approval from Osborn.

Nevertheless, it took a full hour of shouting, swearing, struggling chaos to get all the twelve-mule teams subdued, harnessed, and hitched to their proper wagons. Dick noted with pride that his own wagon was ready to roll before at least two of the veteran teamsters'.

He was snapping the last tug when a stranger rode into the firelight on a big buckskin. Dick glimpsed a lean, dark, handsome face with lively black eyes and long black hair curling down to his shoulders. The newcomer was dressed much like the others except for a fringed deerskin hunting shirt and Indian moccasins. As he swung down to a chorus of shouted greetings, Dick saw that he was under medium height and slender.

Captain Osborn shook hands with the stranger, talked for a

moment, then led him over to Dick's wagon. "Meet your boss, Charles Bent. This is Dick Wootton, fresh from the East, but no greenhorn, Charles."

"His hitch-up proves that," Bent smiled, his handclasp surprisingly strong. "Glad you're with us, Dick."

They moved on, leaving Dick a little dazed at meeting one of the best-known figures in the West. The Bent brothers, in partnership with the aristocratic Frenchman, Ceran St. Vrain, had made Bent's Fort the capital of a gigantic fur and trading empire that molded the course of Western history.

Shortly after four the train moved out, as false dawn tinted the eastern horizon. At seven they halted for breakfast, then rolled on over endless, undulating prairie, broken only by rows of cottonwoods and willows along the streams. The big Santa Fe train was two days ahead, but their lighter, faster wagons would easily catch up before they reached dangerous Comanche country.

Each driver had a helper who rode with him and shared the constant watch for danger. Although this was considered peaceful country, you never knew when a band of hostile savages might decide to raid through it in hopes of striking an unwary train.

Dick's companion was a lanky, garrulous youngster named Jim Hobbs who confided that he was sixteen years old and had run away from a tyrannical stepmother. Jim babbled more than he watched but his company relieved the tedium, so Dick kept an eye on both sides of the trail and let him ramble on.

There was a fleeting moment of excitement in midafternoon when a handful of Indians appeared on a nearby hill. Dick was checking the load in his new rifle when Charles Bent galloped by, shouting, "It's all right, boys. They're only Kaws, thieving nuisances around camp but not hostile."

Dick put his gun down, torn between relief and disappointment. Fighting off a real Indian attack would be the ultimate adventure, something to remember and talk about back in civilized Kentucky. It would be just his luck, Dick thought, to make the whole journey and return home without ever encountering a hostile redskin. He was soon to find out how needless that worry was.

On the fifth day they caught up with the fifty-seven wagons of the Santa Fe train. By that time the character of the landscape was changing, the rolling prairie giving way to high rock ridges and deep, wooded canyons. That night they "forted up" with the wagons in a tight circle, the stock picketed close by under double night guard.

"You're in Comanche country now," Bent told Dick. "From here on, every man's life hangs on eternal vigilance. An attack could come at any time of night or day. Comanches, like the Blackfeet up north, make a sport of torturing prisoners. They're hated and feared by all other tribes, with good reason. So keep a sharp lookout, Dick, and make sure that loose-mouth squirt with you does the same."

Two nights later Dick's name was drawn from the hat for his first turn at night guard. He was aroused at midnight and posted on a rock ridge, just beyond the wagons. "If you see anything moving outside the picket line, or hear a whisper of sound, shoot first and ask questions later. The Comanches like to run off all the stock, leaving a train stranded to be picked off at their leisure."

"Don't worry," Dick said, with more nonchalance than he felt. "Nothing is going to get past me."

Then he was all alone, feeling the silence and the fearful weight of responsibility pressing down on him. The moon had set and the faint starlight gave even the commonest objects a distorted appearance. Dick's mouth felt dry and cottony. He swallowed hard and checked the priming of his Hawken.

Two hours had crawled by when he heard the alien sound. He tensed, hearing the unmistakable rustle of movement, then a faint clatter of dislodged stones. Straining through the darkness, he made out a shadowy blackness moving slowly near the

16

edge of the picketed mules. It seemed low down, like an animal . . . or a crouching Indian. In either case, he had his orders. The Hawken settled against his shoulder and the crash of the shot split the silence. Down the slope, the black object dropped heavily, threshed once, and was still.

At the sound of the shot the whole camp erupted into a tumult of yells as men burst from their blankets, grabbing for their guns. Dick heard Bent's voice bawling, "Night guards, pull back to the wagon line and take cover. Everybody in."

He scuttled back, reloading furiously, to pant out his story. For a full twenty minutes the men crouched behind the barricade of wagons, expecting an attack at any moment. At last Captain Osborn straightened up.

"If it was Injuns, they'd have hit us by now. I'm going out and have a look."

He pulled a glowing stick from the fire, blew it to a bright flame and strode off, a couple of the men at his heels. Dick saw them bend over the fallen object, then a startled yell came back. "It's Old Jack, our best lead mule."

Somehow, the gray mule had pulled his picket pin and come wandering out in search of tender grass. The shot had caught him in the head to put a finish to his wanderings.

The men poured out to look and whoop with relieved laughter, or to growl resentfully at the loss. Someone howled, "Three cheers for the fearless mule-slayer!" Another voice cried, "He saved us from bein' scalped by a savage knothead."

Dick stood with fists clenched, his face hot with shame and embarrassment. He gulped and blurted, "Whatever the mule was worth, I'll pay it back. If I don't have enough cash, I'll work it out."

Charles Bent smiled and patted Dick's shoulder. "Forget it. You followed orders. I'd rather lose ten Old Jacks than have one Comanche get past you, Dick. You did just right."

Dick felt a little better but still horribly embarrassed, and his feelings were not soothed by the rough joshing he had to take from the other teamsters. All through that day he flinched and turned red when a chorus of raucous *hee-haws* broke out from the plodding train.

They forded Little Cow Creek and rolled steadily west and south into ever wilder country. A few nights later they camped by a famous landmark, a towering escarpment known as Pawnee Rock, near the Pawnee Fork of the Arkansas. Double guards were posted and the men slept lightly, for that day they had seen pony tracks and the smoke of Indian signal fires from the hills.

It was around midnight and bright moonlight when Dick was awakened by shots and the cry, "Comanches!" He sprang from his blanket to see a solid mass of painted savages on horseback pounding straight at the aroused camp. A few of the Indians had guns, most of them old firelock fusees that threw a handful of scrap or a huge ball of Mexican copper with wondrous inaccuracy. A majority, however, had steel-tipped arrows and long lances with fourteen-inch blades of steel that could be deadly at close range.

The Comanches had apparently gambled on surprise to let them charge through the demoralized camp, then vanish into the night with the stock. With greenhorn emigrants it might have succeeded. But these were trail-hardened veterans of many an attack who sprang to the shelter of their wagons to pour a deadly fire into the savage ranks.

For all his inexperience and excitement, Dick found his mind cool and his hands steady. Forted up between Bent and Captain Osborn he instinctively obeyed the unwritten law of the frontier, timing his fire with theirs so that never were all three guns empty at the same time.

In the face of the massed fire, the Comanche charge wavered and broke only yards from the wagons. They made two more half-hearted rushes, mainly to snatch up their own casualties from the ground, then melted away into the night.

Charles Bent, his face a dark mask of powder smoke from

18

blowback, finished reloading and grinned at Dick. "You did fine, young fellow. You can trail with me any day in the week."

The fleeing Indians had left three warriors dead on the ground. Dick moved out with the crowd, staring at the glistening painted bodies with mixed feelings. He was fairly certain that his marksmanship had accounted for one or more Comanche casualties. It was the first time he had fired at other human beings and the realization gave him a sense of shock. The shock deepened as Osborn knelt and seized one of the long scalp locks. His knife made a deft circle and the black hair came loose, bound by a patch of skin the size of a silver dollar. Dick swallowed hard and tried to look away as the remaining bodies were similarly scalped.

Rising, Osborn saw his expression. "You better get used to it, Dick. Scalps can be powerful medicine for saving your own life. There's no better way to win the friendship of dangerous Indians than by showing them the scalps of their worst enemies. Since all tribes hate Comanches, these are better than a passport anywhere we go."

The next day Dick forgot his qualms in a new thrill. A small herd of buffalo was encountered close to the trail, the first live ones he had ever seen. The range was extreme but he loaded his Hawken with an extra powder charge, stood on the wagon seat, and picked off a young bull with one shot.

Dick got high praise and a rigorous lesson in skinning and butchering some eighteen hundred pounds of inert flesh. He also got the green hide, which he learned would bring him an extra five dollars at Bent's Fort, and his first feast of buffalo hump, tongue, ribs, and liver.

Young Jim Hobbs, who had blazed away at the herd and completely missed every shot, was frankly and noisily envious of Dick's triumph. "You jest wait," he said over and over. "I'm gonna get me a buffle out of the next herd, and you can bet your hair on that, by golly. I'd have nailed that bull of yourn if you hadn't got in a lucky shot first."

A few days later they reached the Cimarron Crossing and the parting of the ways. Here the Santa Fe train forded the Arkansas and continued on through the sand hills toward the Mexican capital. The seven Bent wagons turned off westward to follow the American side of the river for the remaining hundred and fifty miles to Bent's Fort.

They had little more than lost sight of the larger train when their scouts came pounding in, shouting: "Close up those intervals! Close up, everybody, and keep a sharp lookout. A war party of Comanches is stalking us in those sand hills over across the river."

Tingling with excitement, Dick kept a sharp watch and was rewarded by several glimpses of Indians along the crests of the dunes. They appeared to be keeping pace with the wagons, hoping for an opportunity to make a surprise attack. But small as it was, the Bent party must have looked like tough, competent veterans able to give a good account of themselves, and the night passed without an alarm.

It was nearing noon the next day when the noise of the passing wagons stampeded a lone buffalo bull. He was an old one who had apparently taken refuge from the heat and flies in a dense thicket. Dick's first inkling of his presence was a loud snorting and the crash of underbrush.

The next moment the monstrous brown shape burst out in a blind panic and charged straight through the line of wagons, almost colliding with the leaders of Dick's team. The startled mules were thrown into a squealing, plunging melee. Dick had his hands too full averting a runaway to grab for his rifle.

Yelling with excitement, Jim Hobbs jerked out his old cap-and-ball pistol and fired point-blank. More by luck than skill, the ball found the vulnerable spot on the animal's neck, although the powder charge was too light for a clean kill. The buffalo stumbled to its knees, then scrambled up and ran on, bellowing and shaking its great head. It jumped into the shallow river, throwing up sheets of muddy water with every jump as it lumbered toward the thick screen of willows on the Mexican side.

Above the tumult, Jim was howling crazily, "I hit him! I wounded him!" He lunged for the Hawken between Dick's knees. "Gimme your rifle quick so's I can finish him off."

Dick's hands were occupied. He clamped his legs together to hold the gun. "Let go, you crazy coot! He's already out of range and you know the rule about sticking close to the train."

"He's my first buffle, and I ain't losin' him," Jim yelled, almost in tears. He stopped tugging at the Hawken and leaped to the ground. "Somebody give me a rifle, quick!"

The helper on the next wagon was a boy of about Jim's age named John Baptiste who was the proud possessor of an ancient Brown Bess musket. He sprang down, waving the gun. "Mine's all loaded and ready, Jim. I'll help you run him down."

They ran to the river and went splashing through the waist-deep shallows toward the spot where the wounded bull had already vanished into the willows. Charles Bent, galloping back from his position far ahead of the train, cupped his hands and bawled, "Come back! Come back, you young idiots! The Comanches are right over there in the hills."

Either the boys were too excited to heed him or the noise of their splashing drowned out his warning. Without looking back they dashed through the reed-choked shallows and plunged out of sight into the willow thicket.

Bent whirled, his face grim. "Saddle riding mules and we'll try to catch them in time. I want a couple of first-class trackers and the best rifle shots in the train. Dick, that includes you."

Precious time was lost quieting and saddling the jittery mules but finally Dick and five grim companions were fording the river behind Charles Bent. They wasted a great deal more time following the erratic zigzag trail of the wounded buffalo through the brushy bottom. A full half hour had gone by before they finally broke out onto the open sand barrens.

A half mile back from the river they found the carcass of the dead buffalo lying on its side in the sand. The two missing boys were nowhere in sight. But on the soft, sandy earth, the newspaper of the plains, the story of their fate was written stark and clear for even Dick's untrained eye to read.

The fresh tracks of a dozen or more unshod ponies swept straight down out of the sand hills, formed a broad, trampled circle around the carcass, and then returned to the dunes. Matt Curdy, one of the train scouts, glanced up at the brassy sky and broke the silence.

"Check your priming and look sharp. They was here so recent the vultures haven't even had time to light and pick yet."

Dick glanced up at the low-wheeling shapes overhead and gave the Hawken's breech a sharp bump with the heel of his hand to settle the grains of priming powder. A cold prickle ran down his back. He could almost feel the impact of malevolent black eyes sending shafts of hatred down from the hill-crests.

Charles Bent straightened in the saddle, his face bleak. "There's nothing we can do now. They took the boys alive but they'd kill them in a minute if we tried a rescue attempt. Even if we had a force strong enough to follow and attack, we'd never get them back alive. We'll go back to the train."

They rode close-bunched and alert but there were no signs of Comanche pursuit. Presently Matt Curdy jogged his shaggy pony beside Dick's mule.

"You can quit twisting that bull neck of yours into knots, boy. It ain't at all likely we'll see hide nor hair of those redskins again. They've more than collected the *coups* they was hangin' around for and they'll be bustin' to hurry back to their village and celebrate their glorious victory. Injuns don't see things the way white men do. To a Comanche mind, snaggin' that pair of scared, wet-eared pups is ever' bit as big an honor as whupping the whole lot of us in a fight."

"What . . ." Dick began, then had to stop to swallow a lump in his throat. "What do you figure will become of Jim and John?"

Curdy's pale-eyed glance slid toward him, then away. "It's hard to tell, but if I was you I'd try not to dwell on it, Dick. Generally it ain't good for a feller to ask into Comanche fun unless he has a mighty strong stummick. From the look on your face, I'd say yours ain't exactly in its prime right now."

4

TRUE to Matt Curdy's prediction, the Comanches disappeared immediately and were not seen again. Behind them they left a scar on Dick's spirit that would never wholly heal.

The wagons rumbled steadily westward. They were on the open treeless prairie now, and the days fell into a dreary pattern of heat and dust and monotony. With no one to talk to and little to see, Dick spent the long hours recalling, examining, and sorting the experiences of recent weeks. Everything he had seen or done or heard about from others was carefully filed away in his orderly mind, ready for instant use. In the rare moments when his thoughts drifted back to Kentucky and the tobacco plantation, he was startled to discover how vague and unreal the memories had become.

The train rolled through the Big Timbers, a great silver-green belt of giant cottonwoods, and made final night camp opposite the mouth of the Purgatory River. Their destination lay just over the horizon, a scant twelve miles to the east.

"Well, Dick, the ordeal is almost over," Charles Bent remarked as they sat around the supper fire. "We should reach Fort William around midday tomorrow."

"Fort *William?*" Dick blurted, startled. "But I thought . . ."

Charles smiled wryly. "When our post was built I named it for my brother William, who is officially the resident manager. But right from the first the mountain men insisted on calling it simply Bent's Fort, which is the only name many people have ever heard."

Dick blew a long breath of relief. "I was floored there for a minute, after being set on seeing Bent's Fort tomorrow."

"I hope you aren't disappointed. But I imagine you'll be glad just to have this tiresome trip over with."

"The seat of my pants sure will," Dick admitted ruefully. "I never knew a wagon seat could get so blamed hard. But I wouldn't have missed the experience for anything."

"You pulled your weight like a veteran. Whenever you make up your mind to head back home there'll be a driver's job waiting for you as far as Independence."

"I'm obliged," Dick said, but there was little enthusiasm in his voice. Beyond the fire Matt Curdy chuckled.

"It 'pears to me, Charlie, like our young Mister Wootton has gone and cotched hisself a bad case of prairie fever."

By common consent they cut the last day's nooning short and pushed on through the hammering heat. The afternoon was still young when the outriders far ahead set up a wild whooping, waving their hats and firing off their guns. A murmur of excitement ran along the train. Dick jumped onto the wagon seat, peering ahead through the dust and the heat haze.

Suddenly he caught his first glimpse of Bent's Fort and his breath gusted out. Nothing he had heard in all the talk around the night fires had quite prepared him for the reality. Looming above the vast and empty prairie it made him think of pictures he had seen of medieval castles in Europe.

The fort stood on a gravel bench, some three hundred yards back from the river and facing the east. Massive adobe walls sixteen feet high ran a hundred thirty-seven feet in width by a hundred seventy-eight in depth. Adjoining it on the west was a corral as wide and almost as deep, enclosing wagon sheds and space for four hundred head of stock. Its eight-foot walls were topped by a dense thicket of live cactus whose vicious barbs would repel any intruder.

Rising above the iron-clad gate was a high watchtower where

a sentry with a mounted telescope constantly scanned the prairie. An iron signal bell hung over his head and a large American flag whipped sluggishly from its pole atop the belfry. Down in front of the gate stood a brass field gun that could be run inside at night.

Jutting over the southeast and northwest corners were eighteen-foot round towers pierced with rifle and cannon ports that commanded the walls. A square tower above the southwest corner housed the company clerks. A similar tower over the center of the west wall held the office of the partners and the quarters where they entertained distinguished visitors from the East.

Dick saw sunlight wink from brass gimbals as the telescope swung toward the train. Moments later the field gun boomed out a brass-throated welcome, then a little knot of horsemen came pounding across the prairie to meet them. As they drew closer a shout went up: "It's Colonel St. Vrain himself, in from Taos."

Presently Dick was being introduced to the famous partner of the Bent brothers. Ceran St. Vrain was taller than Charles Bent, solidly built, with lively black eyes dancing above the magnificent whiskers that had earned him the Cheyenne name of Blackbeard.

Although dressed as roughly as his companions, he had the indefinable air of the born aristocrat. Ceran St. Vrain was truly a man of two worlds, who could lead a cotillion or a Comanche chase with equal aplomb. When in St. Louis he wore fine broadcloth and linen and dined with society at the Planter's Hotel on terrapin and frog legs. On the trail he wore greasy buckskins and shared the mountain man's delicacy—raw buffalo liver drenched in bile.

"Dick's going home to Kentucky after a short visit," Charles said as he performed the introduction. "When that happens, we'll be losing a good man, Ceran."

St. Vrain studied Dick sharply, then shook his head, smiling. "I think not, *mon ami*. His eyes have the look of the eagle who has found his wings and has flown as he was meant to fly. Such an eagle does not return to the cage. I predict Monsieur Wootton will remain with us for a very long time."

Dick nodded soberly. "I've about made up my mind to that very thing."

He was introduced to the other riders, three young men of about his own age. Marcellin St. Vrain, with George and Robert Bent, were young brothers of the partners who had recently come West to learn the Indian trade. They greeted Dick warmly and promised a grand buffalo hunt as soon as they returned from a trip to Taos.

The next hours were exciting and memorable to Dick. The arrival of a train at the fort was an event, a break in the dull monotony, and some two hundred employees, their families, and visiting frontiersmen roared out to welcome the wagons. Dick's ears ached from a bedlam of yells and war whoops and exuberant gunshots, while the watchtower bell added its clangor to the din. Dogs barked, mules brayed, cattle bawled, and the fort mascot, a great bald eagle, screamed from his perch above the gate. A flock of strutting peacocks, the first Dick had ever seen, spread astonishing rainbow tails and added their raucous cries to the tumult.

Inside the gate the wagons rolled along a short passageway under the watchtower and emerged through a second gate into the *placita,* the open compound. Surrounding this were adobe buildings that made Bent's Fort literally a self-contained city in the wilderness.

Running the length of the north wall was a two-story block of small apartments with the post dining room and kitchen at one end. The east side was occupied by warehouses and the enormous wedge press for baling furs. Along the other two sides were workshops, storerooms, and additional living quarters. The fort had its own blacksmith, wheelwright, carpenter, harness-maker, and wagon builder. There was even a French tailor who turned out fringed deerskin hunting shirts and leggings.

Hostlers took charge of the teams and a clerk led Dick to

a whitewashed cubicle containing a narrow bunk. "This here's your apartment for as long as you want. When you hear the bell ring twice, just foller the crowd to the dining room. Supper'll be buffalo tongue and ribs, antelope steak, prairie hen, and roast turkey, with fresh bread and butter."

Dick whistled. "You don't mean to say you get that big a choice every meal?"

"That," the clerk said, grinning, "ain't a choice unless you're choosy. It's all on the table and as much as you want. The kind depends on the hunting but nobody gets up hungry. If you crave somethin' extry like mudcat or painter or boiled pup, just fetch it to the cooks. But if you want roast skunk, you got to skin it yourself first somewheres downwind."

"I'll keep that in mind," Dick said dryly, "in case the hankering for it comes over me."

Exploring the fort a little later, Dick encountered the Bents and was introduced to the last of the famous brothers. William was ten years younger than Charles and so slightly built that the Cheyennes had named him Little White Man. Beside Dick's two hundred pounds of brawn he looked almost frail, but his raw courage and physical endurance were becoming legendary.

"Charles tells me you have the makings of a mountain man, Dick, but haven't decided on your future yet. Why not stay on here while you make up your mind? We have enough work to keep you busy and give you valuable experience as well. Then if you decide to winter out here, we'll be glad to outfit you for a trip to the mountains with one of the fur brigades."

"There's nothing in the world I'd like better," Dick said, his eyes glistening.

"Then it's settled. We'll work out details when you come up in the morning to draw your wages for the trip."

That evening Dick followed the crowd up onto the flat roofs to enjoy the cool breeze and caught his first sight of mountains. Northward the snow on Pikes Peak reflected the last light of day. Far to the south the humps of the Spanish Peaks were silhouetted against the sunset. He stared at the scene with awe and wonder until the last pale light of day had vanished.

By the time he rolled into his bunk, his mind was made up. In the morning he would write his parents not to expect him home at least until the following spring.

In the weeks that followed Dick worked harder than ever before in his life and found every moment exciting. He unloaded and loaded wagons and strained his powerful muscles at the big press that rammed hides and furs into compact bales. He often clerked in the trading post, weighing out powder and shot, salt, meal, tobacco, and vermilion for the Indians, learning to judge the value of the pelts and hides and handwork they brought in trade. When other work was slack he joined the hunters who kept the fort larder supplied, earning his dollar a day with the best of them.

He saw Charles Bent and Ceran St. Vrain only occasionally. Most of their time was occupied with operating the wagon trains to Independence and Santa Fe, and with managing the company store in Taos, a six-day ride to the south, where both had married Mexican girls and established homes. William managed the fort and the Indian trade, with the able help of his chief clerk Lucas Murray, a big, irascible Irishman whose lurid vocabulary had earned him the Indian name of Mister Goddamn Murray.

An endless stream of hunters, trappers, traders, scouts, and government agents visited Bent's Fort through the summer. With his knack for making friends, Dick became intimate with them all and pumped them dry of knowledge and experience to add to his own growing store. He became a special friend of Kit Carson who, at twenty-six, was already famed as a frontiersman and Indian fighter.

There were usually one or more villages of friendly Indians camped along the river bank below the fort to trade or simply to visit. Dick spent much of his spare time in their lodges, making friends, trading, learning their age-old tricks of wilderness survival and studying the baffling and capricious Indian character. He quickly became expert in the sign language common to all tribes and picked up a smattering of Cheyenne, Arapaho, and Sioux.

He had not realized what else he was accomplishing until one day William remarked, "You've made a hit with our Indian friends, Dick. They've given you a special name, which is an honor they don't bestow lightly. You're known now as Cut-Hand, from the missing fingers, and they add an Indian word meaning White-Man-Whose-Tongue-Is-Straight. That's something to feel proud of and to cherish."

"I'll be dogged," was all Dick could find to say.

5

Wɪᴛʜ summer sliding into fall the Indians began flocking to Bent's Fort to dicker for their winter supplies. This was the common feature of Indian trade and the most hazardous for the trader.

One and all, Indians were as improvident as butterflies. In the spring they sold their winter's catch of hides and furs, then plunged into an orgy of spending and celebrating that left them flat broke in a matter of days. To them this was a matter of small consequence through the summer when game was plentiful and the weather kind, and more important needs could usually be filled by raiding an enemy village.

But with the first smell of winter in the air, they headed for the trading posts to demand their winter's stock of powder and shot and provisions on credit against their next spring's furs. The hapless trader was forced to comply or lose their vital trade to some more generous or reckless competitor. To hold down their spending and keep his risk to a minimum involved days of noisy bickering and bargaining. Dick sat in on many of these sessions and learned a great deal about the Indian mind and the economics of the fur trade.

Among the first arrivals was Chief Yellow Leg's village of southern Cheyennes, down from their hunting grounds around the headwaters of the Smoky Hill. The chief was a commanding figure, typical of the Cheyennes, who were known throughout the West as the tallest, handsomest, and most fastidious of Plains Indians. His wife Bird Eye was fat and jolly but still retained more than a trace of her girlhood beauty.

Following his usual custom, Dick filled a pack with gifts and small trade items and paid a formal visit to the chief's lodge. While he and Yellow Leg sat cross-legged on opposite sides of a blanket, talking and sharing the friendship pipe, Bird Eye slipped up without a word and carefully mended a rip in the sleeve of Dick's hunting shirt.

When the traditional small talk ended, Dick laid out his few trade items. He had brought knives, beads, fishhooks, a stick of vermilion, some bright-colored cloth, and a tin of Bent's water crackers that were specially baked for the company by a cousin back East. As outright gifts he presented Yellow Leg with a stick of tobacco along with small packets of coffee and sugar for making the "sweet soup" beloved by Indians. For Bird Eye he had an awl and three-sided needles for sewing deerskin and a few brightly colored beads.

As he anticipated, the Cheyennes had a few small personal items to trade, mainly things Bird Eye had saved out or made during the summer wanderings. He acquired a half-dozen beaver skins, or plews, and some beautifully beaded moccasins and leggings.

Suddenly, as Bird Eye was rearranging their pack, Dick's eye was caught by a flash of bright color from the end of a roll. "Wait," he said. "Let me see the blanket."

Yellow Leg hesitated oddly, then nodded. As Bird Eye unfolded the cover of beaded elkskin, Dick caught his breath. Throughout the West the Navajos were justly famed for their tightly woven, boldly patterned blankets. So few found their way into trade channels that a Navajo blanket was a treasure in any Indian lodge. Even a common one, well worn, might bring as much as ten buffalo robes.

But the one Dick held in his hands now was a treasure even among treasures, the work of a true artist. Never had he seen such perfection of weaving or brilliance of colors. The familiar stylized Navajo design had been embellished by unique figures and devices unlike any he had ever seen before. It came to him suddenly that this would be the perfect gift to send to his parents in Kentucky, to give them a hint of the primitive beauty of the West. It might even help them to understand the mystery of why he wanted never to leave this strange brooding country.

"How much trade for blanket?" he asked.

Yellow Leg's lips tightened. He signed to Bird Eye who snatched the blanket and rolled it tenderly back in its cover. He shook his head firmly. "Blanket big medicine. No trade."

The unexpected refusal sharpened Dick's desire. He began pushing trade items across the blanket, adding to his offer each time Yellow Leg shook his head. Abruptly he shoved everything into one pile and added, "I'll throw in an ax, an iron kettle, and a horn of powder."

For a moment the chief hesitated in the face of temptation. Then his jaw set. "No trade."

Clearly, the blanket held some deep spiritual significance stronger than his desire for the white man's treasures. Perhaps its possession had been followed by some unusual good fortune, or its design might have a special religious meaning. In any case, Dick recognized defeat and swallowed his disappointment.

He began packing his remaining trade goods. Then, on impulse, he pushed a heavy scalping knife, the fishhooks, and some of the beads back across the blanket. "We'll trade again some other day. These are presents from Cut-Hand to friends."

When he left Dick bore a truly magnificent gift to temper his disappointment, a hunting shirt beautifully tanned and beaded by the skilled hands of Bird Eye. He also carried a warm feeling of having made staunch friends.

He strode into the *placita* and the mellow mood abruptly vanished. A hulking figure in filthy buckskins was shaking a fist at the fort's colored blacksmith, bawling threats and curses. He whirled at the crunch of Dick's steps on the gravel, small pale eyes glaring above an uncombed tangle of dirty whiskers.

"Oh, it's you, Wootton. I was just getting through yore blacksmith's dumb skull what'll happen to him if my hoss ain't shod and shod proper when I'm ready to leave in the morning."

"I wouldn't worry about that, Carse," Dick said coldly. "I'm sure Sam will do anything to make sure your departure is not delayed."

Noah Carse had ridden in a week before with a string of horses for sale. After getting a fair price, he had continued to hang around, abusing the Bent hospitality and earning the active dislike of everyone at the fort. A foul-mouthed bully, his principal amusement was picking on the clerks and frightening visiting Indians.

He suddenly noticed the hunting shirt. "Ain't that the one old Yellow Leg's squaw made? What'll you take for it?"

"It was a gift and it's not for sale."

"Ain't you the lady-killer, now," Carse sneered. Then his pale eyes sharpened. "Say, you didn't dicker the old skunk out of his medicine blanket, did you?"

Dick went rigid. So Carse had also caught a glimpse of the Navajo piece on one of his trading visits and coveted it. He said bluntly, "I didn't, and you needn't waste time trying, either. The blanket has some sacred meaning to Yellow Leg and he won't part with it for anything."

Carse guffawed coarsely. "You *are* a green pork-eater, boy. When you've been dealin' with stinkin' redskins as long as I have, you'll know there's always ways of getting what you want. I've got a market for that rag and I'll bet you a plew to a plug I'll have it when I ride out of here tomorrow morning."

Dick swung around without replying and went on to his apartment. He was disgusted, but he was also vaguely worried. To think of the strong-willed chief robbed of his proudest possession filled him with sick rage. From what he had seen of the arrogant Carse, there would be no limits to his brutality or trickery.

However, Carse hung around the fort the rest of the day and some of Dick's concern faded. It returned sharply the next morning with the realization that for more than an hour Carse's horse had waited in front of the blacksmith shop, saddled and ready for the trail. He swung abruptly and went in. "Where's Carse?"

"I don't know and don't care," the blacksmith growled. "He

34

went out the gate early, grinning to himself like he was up to big deviltry. I hope he never comes back."

Dick whirled and ran out, driven by a sharp foreboding of disaster. The Cheyenne camp was curiously quiet, with most of the lodge flaps tightly shut. The few Indians in sight turned away without their customary friendly *"How!"* of greeting. The fire in front of Yellow Leg's big lodge was out, the ashes cold.

As Dick lifted the flap a heavy, sweet smell assailed his nostrils. The lodge was thick with the fumes of Indian whiskey, a concoction of raw alcohol and water, frequently flavored with red pepper and tobacco.

Yellow Leg and his wife were sprawled on robes, snoring heavily. On the blanket between them lay two of the heavy clay three-pint cups used in the trade to measure everything from gunpowder to coffee, sugar, and molasses. Beside Bird Eye, the elkskin blanket-wrapper lay open and empty.

A sticky brown film in the bottom of the cups told Dick the bitter story. He knew Indians were passionately fond of sweet syrup. Unscrupulous traders often mixed whiskey with the syrup to conceal the taste. When the Indians were too maudlin to know what was going on, they were cheated and robbed without mercy.

Clearly, Carse had used the same stratagem to steal the medicine blanket. Knowing the attitude of Bent & St. Vrain toward the whiskey trade, he had cached his supply somewhere outside the fort and dug it up for this purpose. Unless he could be intercepted in time, he would vanish into the wilderness with his prize and the blanket might never be seen again.

His big fists clenched and his eyes hot, Dick burst out of the lodge and charged up the slope. The sentry in the watchtower leaned out to call something, but Dick was blind and deaf to everything but the driving need to stop Carse. He plunged along the shadowy tunnel and into the glare of sunlight from the graveled surface of the *placita*. His pent breath gusted out at the sight of Carse in front of the blacksmith shop.

The big trader stood by his horse, holding the Navajo medicine blanket open and boasting loudly of his prowess to a knot of silent onlookers. At Dick's explosive entrance his head jerked around and the small eyes went wary. Moving with exaggerated slowness he folded the blanket and hung it over his saddle, his narrowed gaze never leaving the approaching figure.

When Dick was close and coming on in purposeful silence, Carse let his mean slash of mouth curl into a sneer. "You owe me a plug of chaw, sonny. I told yuh there was ways to get a trade when you know how."

"I just saw *your* way," Dick said through his teeth.

"That's how you farmers learn the tricks of the trade." He studied Dick's set face and the blazing anger in his eyes, and his own mask of coarse humor slipped away. "Now you wouldn't be thinkin' of trying to do somethin' about it, would you?"

"Yes," Dick said. "I'm taking the medicine blanket back to its rightful owner, the man you stole it from."

"Oh, are you, boy?" Carse's voice dropped to a venomous murmur. "To do that, boy, you fust got to take it away from me."

"I aim to," Dick said, and dropped into a crouch.

Carse's right hand whipped behind and reappeared gripping his butchering knife. It was a murderous weapon, bone-handled, its ten-inch blade whetted to razor sharpness on the curving edge, the straight edge thick and heavy enough to crack buffalo bones or an opponent's skull. He held it with the practiced skill of a veteran knife-fighter, waist-high, the blade jutting up and out from his fist. His left arm was out and slightly bent, thick fingers curved into talons, ready to parry a thrust, grab a wrist, or claw out his opponent's eyes.

"Get on with the takin', sonny. I got a long trail ahead of me afore sundown and you're holdin' me up."

Dick's own Green River butcher knife was on his hip but he made no move to draw it. He had come through his full share of vicious slugging, butting, gouging, stomping frontier fights, but he had never dueled with knives and he felt infinitely more confidence in his big fists.

36

He began a slow, wary circling, drawing the other out into the open, away from his horse and the hitchrack and other impedimenta of the blacksmith shop. He was only vaguely aware that they were surrounded by a tense crowd of silent spectators as virtually everyone in the fort dropped his work and ran to watch the fight.

For so big a man, Carse was light on his feet and fast as a striking snake. Without warning he lunged like a swordsman, the knife aimed to strike Dick's belly and slash upward in a murderous disemboweling stroke.

Fast as he was, Dick was a shade faster. His left hand caught the knife wrist and forced it downward. Simultaneously his right fist drove a smashing blow full into the biceps of that arm. He felt the bulging muscle tissue roll and squash out under the punishing impact, felt the whole arm go limp in temporary paralysis. He gave the wrist a snapping twist and Carse's knife flew out of his numbed grasp. Someone kicked it out of sight under the feet of onlookers.

Dick let go and got in a sledging left to the matted whiskers before they broke apart. Carse was sobbing curses, working his right shoulder frantically in an effort to restore life to the limp arm. He crabbed sideways to escape Dick's charge, flailing his left arm in defense. Dick beat it aside and hammered in blows, feeling a tooth give and nose cartilage collapse under his iron-hard knuckles. Carse's left fist pounded him with blows that rocked but lacked the steam to stun him.

The big man suddenly leaped forward, feinted with his left, and launched a vicious kick. Dick twisted, taking the blow on his hip. Then, before Carse could recover balance, he caught the raised leg and jerked upward with all his strength. Yelling, Carse flew into the air in a half somersault and slammed down on the back of his neck with an impact that jarred the ground. He made a feeble, aimless effort to roll over, then collapsed with his mouth open.

It was not until the whooping crowd swarmed on him, pump-

37

ing his hands and pounding his back, that Dick fully realized the fight was over and he had won. He felt no sense of triumph, only an aching weariness and the lingering dregs of his anger.

"I'm taking the blanket back to Yellow Leg," he rasped. "If Carse wakes up in a mood to try again, I'll be happy to accommodate him when I come back."

The scout Matt Curdy laughed. "I'm thinkin' you won't see hide nor hair of that skunk. You knocked the fight and the cussedness plumb out of him for one day, and done it as quick and purty as any I ever seed."

Dick pushed through the throng and got the blanket from Carse's saddle. At the wash trough in front of the dining room he plunged his whole head into the tepid water, feeling it clear away some of the cobwebs from his brain. He was mopping his face on a torn sleeve when he heard the crunch of hoofs on the gravel.

He looked up, startled to see Charles Bent lounging in his saddle. From the thick layers of trail dust and the drying lather on the horse's flanks, he had just come in from Taos. His bronzed face, trained by years of matching wits with Indian bargainers, was devoid of expression. Beyond him, Dick saw the slight figure of William Bent leaning out the window of their tower quarters, directly above the scene of the fight.

It came to him suddenly that the brothers Bent might not take kindly to having their authority usurped and a customer beaten up by a minor employee. He squared his shoulders and braced himself for a reprimand, or worse.

The dark mask of Charles' face broke into a smile. "The next time you put on an exhibition of skill like that, Dick, I'd appreciate some advance notice. If I'd arrived a few minutes later I'd have missed this one completely, and it was well worth seeing."

6

THE day after the fight a clerk found Dick tallying hides in the warehouse under the east wall. "You're wanted up in the tower. Mister William said for you to drop whatever you're doing and come as soon as you can."

Dick stopped only long enough to wash up at the trough, then climbed the stairs with a feeling of lively expectancy. A visit to the famous aerie was an occasion in itself. He had seen it only once before when he went to collect his wages, and had been awed nearly speechless by its elegance. Here the partners entertained visiting dignitaries and wealthy sportsmen from the East and no expense had been spared in its furnishings.

William was at his desk, checking some sort of list, with Charles leaning over his shoulder. He nodded a greeting. "Make yourself comfortable. We're almost finished with this."

Dick welcomed the chance to look around the big room with fresh wonder. The floor was carpeted, the whitewashed walls hung with colorful Indian handiwork. There were easy chairs and cushioned benches, racks of books and sporting arms and the only billiard table west of the Mississippi. Behind the desk stood shelves of ledgers and letter-books and a large iron safe. On the wall hung Charles' government trading license, dated December 18, 1833, for which he had posted a two thousand dollar bond.

The plank shutters were swung wide and through the open windows Dick could see Pikes Peak and a Cheyenne hunting party trotting off across the sear brown prairie. Upriver the fort's livestock grazed on the bottoms under the watchful eye of armed herders. A hot breeze brought the hum of activity and the stench of raw hides from the *placita*. His throat tightened with a surge of emotion for which he could find no words.

He was recalled to the present by the scratch of the pen as William initialed the paper and pushed it aside. "Dick, you have learned enough about the trade in the short time you've been here so we don't have to tell you beaver prices are dropping and competition is getting stiffer. We've been fortunate in holding the loyalty of the southern Cheyennes and Arapahoes, but we're too far south to get much trade from the northern Cheyennes and their Sioux allies. They range mainly above the South Platte."

Dick nodded in silent comprehension, his eyes bright with interest. Charles perched on a corner of the desk and took up the recital. "We've just learned that our strongest rival, the AFC —John Jacob Astor's American Fur Company—has bought Fort Laramie on the North Platte. That gives them an ideal spot to dominate the northern trade and even lure away some of our southern business, unless we act fast to block them."

"That'll be tough," Dick said thoughtfully, "short of building a post of your own up there too."

"That's in the cards for next year," William said, "but we have decided on more immediate action. Indians usually wait until spring to take their winter's catch to the post for trade. We plan to send a trading caravan around to their villages and skim off the cream of their peltry this fall and winter, right under the nose of AFC. It will be arduous and possibly dangerous, but it can set competition back long enough for us to get a more permanent toehold."

Dick was silent, his thoughts in a turmoil. Clearly they wanted him to join the expedition, and his own thirst for adventure urged him to go. But that meant a year's postponement of his own plan to join a trapping brigade and wrest a fortune in beaver from the wilderness. He swallowed hard. "If you're asking me to drive one of the wagons, I'll do it."

Charles smiled faintly. "That wasn't quite what we had in mind, Dick. We want you to command the expedition."

"Me?" Dick gasped. "Command? But . . . but I'm only a Ned—a greenhorn. I can't even tell a Sioux from a Kaw yet."

"But you learn fast," William said. "You have a keen eye, a cool head, and an open mind. You know sign language and the mechanics of trade and you've won the confidence of the Indians. Your fight on behalf of Yellow Leg will be known and talked of in every lodge on the Plains. We think you can cut the mustard, and both Ceran and Kit Carson agree."

"Also," Charles added quietly, "you've shown yourself to be a sharp trader as well as a fair one and this is, after all, a commercial venture. So what do you say, Dick?"

Dick let his breath out slowly. "It looks like you've said about all of it for me. When do I leave?"

They breakfasted at three in the morning, to the annoyance of Charlotte, the Bents' colored cook. Dick had hoped for an early start but the mules, too long out of harness, were skittish and balky and the catch-up took well over an hour. Dawn was breaking before the last of the ten teams was hitched in a bedlam of yelling, swearing, braying, and jangling of chains and harness bells. The reserve and pack animals were dragged and prodded to the lead line behind the last wagon.

Dick made a last circuit of the ten big Pittsburgh wagons, tugging at cover lashings, rapping water casks, squatting to see that spare hardwood tongues and axles and reaches were properly slung under the beds. He stood for a moment, running his mind over a thousand and one details, feeling the weight of responsibility heavy on his shoulders.

The Sioux were scattered over what is now northern Colorado, Wyoming, and Nebraska, in isolated villages that picked up and moved with the buffalo herds. To find them and trade out their stock might take as long as a year. Meanwhile, some five thousand dollars of Bent & St. Vrain investment, together with the lives and well-being of thirteen men, would be in his care and keeping.

He straightened his shoulders and walked to where the Bents stood quietly watching. He had seen little of them in the last hectic days of preparation. Once details had been agreed upon, they had left him alone to make his own decisions, not badgering him with advice. He felt a warm glow of appreciation for their tactful show of confidence.

"We're all set to roll."

"Best of luck," William said, and Charles added, "If you should get in a tight spot, just remember that goods can be replaced but men's lives can't." They shook hands soberly and parted.

Dick tramped to where a hostler waited with his horse and rifle. His two scouts, Matt Curdy and Dan Wyler, slouched on their Indian ponies, moccasined feet out of the stirrups and dangling almost to the ground. Their worn buckskins, black with grease and smoke and dried blood, made Dick painfully conscious of the newness of his own. He hoped a couple of days on the trail would make this less conspicuous.

He started to mount and stopped, frowning. "Somebody has switched saddles on me. This isn't the one I picked out."

Matt Curdy unloaded a gob of tobacco juice and nodded. "I done it, Dick. Yourn had iron stirrups and they're plain p'ison for freezin' to a feller's feet in cold weather. Wood stirrups like them are the ticket fer winter."

"I'm obliged to you, Matt," Dick said.

He swung up, taking a last sharp look along the train. The drivers were ready, jerklines taut. Limpy Brey, the cook and handyman, dozed on the seat of the lead wagon, his chest and kettles lashed to the tailgate. A large leather sack hung open underneath to receive any buffalo chips picked up along the way. Later, on stretches of treeless prairie, these would provide the only fuel for their fires.

Dick raised his voice. "On account of the late start, we'll skip the nooning stop and go into night camp early. The loads will likely shake down some and that will give us daylight to do any needful tightening up or repacking."

He lifted his arm high. From the watchtower came the sentry's cry, "All clear on the prai-reeee!" and the iron-shod gate creaked open. Dick's arm slashed forward. *"Str-r-retch out!"* Whips cracked, drivers yipped, and the train creaked into motion.

They rounded the fort and rolled westward up the flat Arkansas bottoms through the brightening day. Past the corral, Dick brought the wagons up into a double line, two abreast. In case of Indian attack the men could cover each other and swing into a tight defense circle more quickly than could a straggling single line. Also, being able to talk back and forth would help stave off boredom.

Dick turned to the scouts. "Do you think it's too soon to start scouting ahead?"

"That's somethin' it's never too soon for," Curdy said. "Especially along here. The Bents set their fort where the hunting grounds meet to be handy to more tribes, but to my notion it's too dang handy. You never know when a passel of Utes or Comanches or Pawnees'll drop by, looking for scalps. We've even had Blackfeet and Snakes, and last fall some Prairie 'Paches killed and scalped a hay-cutter not five hundred yards from the wall."

They jabbed heels into the flanks of their ponies and cantered on ahead. Curdy slanted off to follow the riverbank, his sharp eyes probing the rushes and the thickets of willow and wild grape along the water's edge. Wyler swung right to the line of chalk banks and rocks where the high rolling prairie dropped abruptly to the flat river bottoms. Here the runoff from melting snow and torrential rains had cut deep gullies that could easily conceal a war party.

Dick took a position ahead of the train and near enough to swing back and take command at the first sign of danger. As he rode his restless eyes searched endlessly for a flash of movement, a thread of smoke, the sudden startled flight of birds, or a dark speck that might be an Indian's lifted head. The sights and sounds and smells of the land opened to his senses like the turning pages of a book. The rising sun warmed his back and a soft wind fanned his face and he felt more strong and free and completely alive than ever before in his life.

7

At Fountain Creek, that tumbles down from a shoulder of Pikes Peak to join the Arkansas, the train turned north, skirting the foothills of the Rockies. They had made excellent time so far, but from here on the ground would be more broken, the traveling slower.

Autumn was laying its hold on the land. The aspen leaves had already turned their flaming yellow and the thickets were bright with the colors of ripe berries and fruits. The air was crisp and dry, the nights frosty. Dick was in a fever of impatience to get beyond the South Platte into the Sioux hunting grounds before winter caught them, but there was no hurrying the mules and he had to count fifteen miles a good day's travel.

Buffalo had been plentiful, with Dick and the scouts taking turns "running meat," making the daily kills. One day they had found the prairie dotted with small bands of thirty to a hundred buffalo, each ringed by its circle of slavering white buffalo wolves waiting to pull down the weak or unwary. This was the beginning of the "running season" when the scattered bands would drift together to form the immense migrating herds that shook the earth with the thunder of their passage.

That day they laid over to "make meat," putting up a generous supply against the inevitable lean days ahead. When they moved on, every wagon and every team was festooned with thin ribbons of meat drying in the sun to become that imperishable mainstay of the frontiersman, "jerky." The Indians pounded this up with mashed wild cherries and marrow and molded cakes that were compact, tasty, nourishing, and would keep indefinitely.

So far the only Indians they had encountered were a band of Arapahoes on their way to Bent's Fort. But now they were skirting the country of the Mountain Utes and every man was on the alert. At night they forted up the wagons with the right front wheel of one chained to the left rear of the next, and each team picketed to its own rig. Night guards were doubled and the shifts cut to two hours to make sure each man stayed awake and sharp.

Dick was standing watch in the small hours of a morning when a coyote's eerie, haunting, "Yip-yip-yip-owooooo!" came from the nearby darkness. Another wailed in the distance and the mules set up a nervous stirring.

Matt Curdy materialized suddenly from the shadows. "What did you think of them cayutes, Dick?"

"I'd as soon they didn't sing, Matt. When a whole pack is howling, it's just a racket. But a loner like that sounds so kind of lost and sadlike it makes my hair lift."

"You be keerful it don't lift right off'n your head, boy. Them two cayutes wears moccasins and breechclouts, and liftin' hair is their idee of proper sport."

In one swift movement Dick had his rifle up and the hammer thumbed back. "How could you tell, Matt? They sounded like the real critter to me."

"Dogged if I know, Dick. But when you've heerd as many of 'em as I have you jest feel the difference. And notice how the mules are fussin' up. Cayutes don't bother them jug-ears much but they can smell Injun a mile away. You look sharp while I wake up the rest. Dan's watching t'other side and the redskin ain't been borned who can sneak up on him."

The mules were stamping and snorting, pulling at their picket ropes. The moon was down but the stars gave enough light to reveal any movement near the camp. Without taking his eyes from the open ground, Dick hauled his powder horn around and pulled the stopper with his teeth. He tipped his Hawken, dumping out the priming, pouring a fresh charge into the pan as a precaution against a misfire. It was probably unnecessary in this high country where there was no night dew to dampen the powder but he had learned early that on the frontier the man who stayed alive was the man who took no needless chances.

Suddenly, a few yards beyond the shying mules, a moving shadow caught his eye. It was only vague movement, without identifying shape, and for a fleeting moment Dick's mind flicked to the night he had shot Old Jack, the lead mule. The memory was still only half formed when the Hawken leaped to his shoulder and crashed.

There was an audible grunt, a brief noisy threshing, and then the shadow was gone, melted into the night. At his elbow, Matt Curdy's whisper said, "Gut-shot, I'm thinkin'. Now we'd best pull back behind the wagons till we see how many they is and how nervy they feels."

Reloading by touch, Dick followed the scout, ducking under a wagon. He sensed rather than saw the other men, each behind his rig with rifle ready. Dick found a place beside Dan Wyler.

"Keep a few rifle balls in your mouth," the scout advised in a soft mumble, "same like I'm doin'. Bein' wet'll make 'em stick to the powder so's you don't have to stop to patch every load. Have you got your two pups on you?"

Dick touched the two single-shot pistols tucked into his belt with his knife and hatchet. "Loaded and ready, Dan."

They waited tensely but there were no more signs of enemies and gradually the mules quieted down. Dawn came at last and the gray light showed the countryside empty of danger. It was Curdy who found and followed the trail of blood spots on the trampled grass to a nearby ravine. He returned presently, shaking his head.

"I be dogged if them wasn't Pawnee moccasins. A passel of young bucks, likely, out to win theirselves some glory stealin' Ute ponies or whatever. Four of 'em came and four of 'em left, but one is a mighty sick Injun. That there shootin' eye of yourn is right sharp, Dick, and it's a good thing. If you hadn't took the fun out of it quick, we'd likely have lost half our mules."

Four days later they found their first Sioux. The scouts cut the sign in the early morning, a small campsite with the feathery ashes of the night fire not yet scattered by the wind. Ranging through the brush, Curdy came upon a broken arrow shaft from which the head had been removed. He studied it and nodded. "It's Sioux, sure enough."

"How can you tell?" Dick asked.

"She's cut flat across at the butt and beveled on the sides of it, an' that's Sioux doin's fer sartain. Every tribe makes its arrers different. Cheyennes allus whittle theirs to a sharp ridge at the butt and paint wavy lines along the shaft so's the spirit-power can guide it straight. Crow shafts is a lot thicker and Pawnees don't bevel the butt. This here's none but Sioux." He fitted the broken pieces together and whistled softly. "An' a big feller he was, too. Or leastwise, mighty long-armed. Injuns cut the shaft to reach from their own armpit to their fingertips. This'n had the longest reach I ever seed."

Dick nodded soberly. "If Sioux come that big, I'm just as glad they're friendly."

"But don't never bet your life on that. An Injun's feelin's can change quicker'n a lightnin' flash in a gully-washer. The only one you can allus depend on is a Comanche. He was born p'ison-mean and he don't never change."

They moved on, the scouts ranging far ahead. About noon Dick saw them riding back side by side. Their pace was unhurried but something in the set of their shoulders gave a silent shout of alarm.

Then he saw the Indians. They appeared suddenly along a ridge line, seven of them sitting their ponies like bronze statues, naked torsos glistening in the noon sun. One figure, towering above the rest, could only be the owner of the oversized arrow.

"You wanted Sioux, boy," Wyler said as they rode up, "and you've got 'em. Oglallas, I'd say, or mebbe Brules, on a hunt.

Leastwise they ain't painted or geared for war, but that don't mean they won't lift scalps if they see the chance. They could be alone, or there could be a thousand more hid behind that ridge."

Dick studied the immediate terrain and lifted a hand to halt the train. "We can't either talk or fight at this distance. I'd say this is as good a place as any to wait for 'em to decide which they want."

Time seemed to drag interminably without movement. Then abruptly the line of Sioux surged forward and down the slope at a headlong run. As they drew closer, Dick could see that only two appeared to have guns, the rest bows and lances. A quarter of a mile from the wagons the Indians pulled in their ponies, forming a milling group almost lost in a great cloud of dust.

Wyler blew out an explosive breath. "It's palaver they've got on their minds—leastwise to begin with." He squinted into the dust. "That big galoot's got the chief's feather in his hair so he'll be the one to make talk with."

"I'll meet him," Dick said. "You'd better come with me, Dan. You speak enough Sioux to fill in my sign-talk." He raised his voice. "The rest of you sit tight. Don't make a show of your guns but be ready to cover us if anything goes wrong."

"Empty your gun in the air to show you come peaceable," Wyler said softly, "but be dang sure them two pups in your belt are primed and cocked, boy. An' stay clear o' that big feller's reach. I'd sooner get hugged by a grizzly than squoze by him."

Firing their rifles skyward they rode out, with Dick in the lead, to meet the giant chief midway between the two parties. He rode alone, empty hands raised, and as they drew together Dick sucked in a sharp breath.

The chief was young, handsome, and splendidly formed, but built on a prodigal scale. Dick estimated that dismounted he would stand at least six feet ten in his moccasins. Twin braids of black hair hung down over a massive bronze chest seamed with scars of battle.

Dick smiled and held up his left hand with its missing fingers.

He slashed his right finger across it, making the Cut-Hand sign. Then bunching the fingers, he touched his breast and his lips and finished by thrusting the fingers toward the chief. In sign language his gesture said: "I, Cut-Hand, speak to you."

The young giant spoke in deep, rolling gutturals. His big hands duplicated the signs Dick had made, except that at the end only two fingers were extended tight together and thrust forward from his lips.

Wyler answered in Sioux and they talked at length. When he turned, the scout was grinning in open relief. "Dick, whuppin' that skunk Carse was the best job you ever done. They know all about it and it set you up proper as a friend of the Red Man who speaks with a straight tongue. That was the sign he made with two fingers together in front of his mouth. If the fingers was spread, it'd mean you got a forked tongue and they wouldn't trust you. The big feller's name is Walks-In-Clouds, which is fitten fer a hoss that stands as tall as he does."

He broke off for another long exchange, while Dick listened carefully, trying to follow the drift of conversation by the few words of Sioux he could recognize. Wyler interrupted at last with a slicing gesture and turned again to Dick.

"I'll tell you somethin' else you got besides a straight tongue, young feller. You got luck, and plenty of it. These bucks is from Snow's village of Oglallas which ain't but three hours from here. He'll lead us there. It's too early in the season for prime beaver, o' course, but he says they've got a plenty of robes and ponies to trade."

They smoked the pipe of friendship, sitting cross-legged on Dick's Mackinaw blanket in the shade of their horses. Walks-In-Clouds brought out his ornately carved pipe, fashioned from red pipestone quarried in the sacred mine up in Minnesota. He packed the bowl with *kinnikinik,* a fragrant mixture of tobacco and the inner bark of the red willow, and offered smoke to the earth and sky and the four directions before handing it across to Dick to seal the pact.

50

Afterward, riding back to the wagons, Wyler said, "Dick, it's plain you've got three things a feller needs most to make good in the trade. You got a knack for gettin' on with redskins, along with a streak o' natural-borned luck, an' the one is ever' bit as needful as t'other."

"You said *three* things, Dan. What's the third?"

Wyler grinned dryly. "That's the one'll help you keep your hair as long as the good Lord intended. It's that dead-center shootin' eye of yourn."

8

THE village of Chief Snow—whose Sioux name meant White-Feathers-Fall-From-Sky—stood in a wooded valley beside a small turbulent stream. The lodges were ranged in a horseshoe, open to the east, the dressed skins a pale yellow-white in the lengthening shadows of afternoon. In front of each the owner's shield and weapons hung on a tripod of poles. Almost every foot of space between the lodges was occupied by drying racks draped with strips of meat being sun-cured for winter.

As Dick and Wyler rode in from the wagon camp a mile upstream, squaws peered out through the lodge flaps in bright-eyed curiosity while hordes of naked children took refuge among the racks, darting quick, giggling looks at the visitors. A pack of half-savage dogs charged out to rage at them from a cautious distance.

Chief Snow's lodge was larger than the others and it was the only one decorated with painted designs. As they dismounted before it, Dick murmured, "Kick me if you see me doing something wrong, Dan. They're so blame touchy about formalities I could make some fool mistake that would set them against us."

"You'll do fine, Dick. Just remember it ain't proper Injun etiquette to walk between a hoss and his fire, or to make talk before you've smoked his pipe and et his grub."

A young Indian boy took their horses. Dick hoisted a pack of presents, drew a deep steadying breath, and lifted the lodge flap.

A fire burned in the center of the lodge and a fat squaw hung over it, stirring a kettle that gave off good food smells. Chief Snow sat on a buffalo robe near the back, with two more robes spread in the place of honor at his left. There was no guessing his age. His skin was seamed with wrinkles and old scars but his eyes were sharp and youthful. Thick plaits of black hair hung over both shoulders and down to his lap.

Dick and Wyler said *"How!"* and shook his hand solemnly before taking seats on the robes. The pipe was loaded and smoked in silence. While he was tapping the ashes carefully back into his pouch, Dick laid packets of sugar and coffee out on the robe. The woman snatched them and waddled back to the fire, making little cooing sounds of pleasure.

She put the kettle between them and they ate, using their own knives to spear chunks of fat meat, scooping the succulent gruel with a single elkhorn spoon passed back and forth. Later, Dick learned the tasty stew contained mashed cherries, gelatinous scraping from buffalo hide, and lichens that grew on old tree trunks.

When the kettle was empty, he broke the silence. "Tell him Cut-Hand comes as a friend, bringing presents for his red brother, the chief."

He laid out his gifts. For the chief he had a navy blue blanket, a whetstone, tobacco, powder, flints, and a small bar of Galena lead for molding shot. For his wife there was red calico, a hand mirror, needles, an awl, and chips of iridescent abalone shell for making ornaments.

The old man's deep-throated voice stopped and Wyler translated. "Cut-Hand is known as a white brother whose heart is good and whose tongue is straight. It is told in the lodges how Cut-Hand's arm was strong against the Bad Face who would cheat the Indian. He is welcome in the lodge of the red brother whose gifts are poor but whose heart is full."

He signed that the robes on which they sat were gifts. His wife brought each a prime beaver plew and moccasins worked with porcupine quills. When they had admired the presents,

Dick said, "Tell him Cut-Hand has many fine and useful articles to trade for the robes and furs and ponies of his red brothers. He asks that a lodge be chosen for trading and a warrior appointed to watch over the goods."

"You're set," Wyler reported after more talk. "He says you can use this lodge and his son-in-law Lone Crow will be the guard."

"It is good." Dick got to his feet. "We will return in the morning with goods and a handsome uniform for Lone Crow. Trading will begin when the sun stands at the top of the sky."

As they jogged back to camp, Wyler belched and patted his stomach. "That was the tastiest pup my meat-bag has knowed in many a moon."

"P-pup?" Dick blurted, feeling his throat close.

"I'll be danged! You mean you didn't know you was eatin' boiled dog?" He shook his head. "You better get to like it, because it's an Injun's idee of a fancy feast to serve visitors."

By midmorning two mule-loads, some five hundred pounds of carefully selected trade goods, were laid out along one side of Snow's lodge. Young Lone Crow guarded them, strutting proudly in his new uniform—a scarlet militia jacket with epaulets and gilded sword, topped by a stovepipe hat sporting a red turkey feather. By white standards the costume was ludicrous, but to the Indian eye it was a proud and handsome symbol of responsibility. The warrior so signally honored would guard a trader's goods with his life if need be.

A constant stream of visitors came to meet Dick, to smoke and talk and sip the sweet coffee he offered with a small present of tobacco, an awl, or perhaps a flint and steel. Walks-In-Clouds came, dwarfing the lodge with his great bulk, followed by other lesser chiefs and Old Men Counselors. Dick conversed in signs and even tried his tongue at the rough Sioux language with modest success.

Promptly at noon the village crier's voice rang out, announcing the opening of trading. Dick spread a blanket and sat down behind it. His first commercial trading venture was on.

The squaws came first, the men hanging back to see how the dealing went and to decide which of the fabulous treasures they most wanted. Dick quickly discovered that with his other qualifications, a trader must have endless patience.

Each woman opened her pack with maddening slowness. Then she must hold and stroke and study each fur or skin before reluctantly laying it on the blanket. Dick would judge its value and toss down a number of small painted "trading sticks" to represent his offer. She would indignantly snatch back her fur or skin and a period of noisy bartering would ensue. But once an agreement had been reached, the price was considered established and the trading progressed more briskly.

When all her goods had been exchanged for sticks, Dick had an interminable wait while she decided what to buy with them. This involved endless fingering of axes, knives, tools, blankets, capes, cloths, beads, and all the other items until she made her choice. Then another took her place and the whole lengthy process was repeated. At dusk trading was suspended for the day and the accumulated peltries packed on the mules to be taken to the wagons.

At the end of a week's trading they had the cream of the village offering, including a string of sturdy ponies, and were ready to push on. With clear directions to the next village, they need waste no time in hunting their next customers and they set out in high spirits.

Thereafter they made good time, moving steadily northward village by village while their stock of goods diminished and the load of peltries grew. At each village they camped some distance away while Dick rode in to establish relations and find out if the Sioux were in a trading mood. His reputation preceded him and he found eager customers at every stop.

They made a wide detour to the east, cutting along the edge of the Nebraska sand hills to avoid Fort Laramie and plunged into the broken country above the North Platte. In what Dan Wyler insisted was further evidence of Dick's "natural-borned luck," winter struck them late and lightly, at first.

Before the heavy snows came they had time to pick an ideal wintering site in a valley sheltered on the north but open to the sun on the south. There was ample wood and water and a fine stretch of open slope, exposed to wind that would keep the grass swept clear of snow so their stock could graze. They put up a snug log shanty in a little side canyon that made a splendid sun-trap, with a backdrop of rock to hold and reflect warmth.

Here they wintered in almost indecent comfort. Between the storms they hunted widely, packing in buffalo and antelope and venison to be stored on racks above the reach of wolves or slowly smoked over fire pits. When the northers howled, they lazed in snug comfort, yarning and mending clothes and making moc-casins, living on their accumulated meat stores.

During a week of January thaw they built a crude wedge press to compact their bulky robes into more portable bales. This was a square crib of logs in which a stack of robes was piled. By hammering long wedges in between the logs on alternating sides, the robes were compressed to less than half their original bulk and lashed with green rawhide strips that would shrink tighter as they dried.

With the first break of spring they were out and heading south again, trading out the last of their stock in the first village they struck. Adding up his accounts of the venture, Dick felt a deep satisfaction. Gauging by prices that had prevailed when they set out, he estimated that he would return twenty-five thousand dollars' worth of peltry and horses to Bent & St. Vrain.

Every river and rivulet was in full roaring flood with its runoff of the winter's snow, making their progress slow and arduous. So spring was sliding into summer by the time they reached the Arkansas and turned east for the homestretch run to Bent's Fort, a scant sixty-five miles downriver.

Spirits were high and long after dark they lounged around

the fire, smoking and talking. One night Matt Curdy was spinning a long tale of a journey with Blackfoot John Smith. Dick lay back on the bare ground, listening in drowsy content.

He turned his cheek against the fragrant grass and suddenly stiffened. His sharp hiss interrupted the story.

"Shhh! Don't anybody make a sound." He pressed his ear tight to the ground, catching a steady, rhythmic pulsing that was more a vibration than a sound, transmitted by the earth. "Horses, and a lot of them, coming this way fast. Scatter the fire and get behind your wagons."

A kick scattered the blazing sticks, cutting the firelight to a dull glow. The thunder of hoofs was clearly audible now, coming from the graveled bottoms downriver.

Dick was checking the priming of his rifle when a familiar voice bawled from the darkness: "Halloo, wagons! Hold fire and identify yourselves."

Dick's lungs emptied in a wild, whooping yell of pleasure. "Colonel St. Vrain! It's Dick Wootton's train, bound for the fort."

Then they were pounding out of the night, a great surging mass of riders, swarming around the corralled wagons, swinging down to shake hands with the drivers and scouts. Dick was more than a little startled to recognize most of the fort employees and a majority of the hunters, traders, and trappers who were usually to be found there at this season. Every man was armed to the teeth and their greetings were strangely restrained.

Someone had hastily restored the fire and by its light he saw St. Vrain's face set in a mask of cold anger. As they shook hands, Dick asked, "What happened to bring all you fellows out this way and where are you bound?"

"We're bound for Taos," St. Vrain said through his teeth, "and we're after blood and Mexican scalps. A courier just rode in this morning with the news that Charles Bent and the other Americans in Taos have been arrested. They're charged with being Texas spies, plotting to arm the Pueblo Indians for a massacre so they can seize New Mexico. We're on our way to rescue them if they're still alive. If they've been harmed, I promise there won't be a building standing or a Spaniard left alive in the valley."

As Dick listened, the first shock of disbelief gave way to anger. "I'm going with you. Matt and Dan can take the train on in, or the drivers can stay forted up and wait right here."

"Come along and welcome, Dick. There'll be work for every rifle we can get if those skunks have made good their talk of a quick hanging."

They were up and on the way by three in the morning, pounding through the starlit bottoms with a recklessness born of their white-hot rage. Below the mouth of Fountain Creek they splashed across the shallow Arkansas and plunged into the burning heat of the Mexican sandhill country.

Twice during the day they saw Mexican riders who watched from distant hills and then disappeared at a gallop. Some of the men were all for giving chase but St. Vrain flatly forbade it.

"Let them go. If they can get word of our coming to Taos early, so much the better. The Mexicans know how mountain men fight and shoot. When they find out close to a hundred of us are on the way, they'll think twice before harming Charles or any other American."

They plunged from burning desert into the wooded foothills and camped on Greenhorn Creek, below the Spanish Peaks. Ahead lay Sangre de Cristo Pass, then the old Yutaw Trail skirting the pine-clad ridges down the San Luis Valley to Taos. Dawn found them laboring up the trail to the Pass, shivering and panting in the high mountain air.

The first rays of the rising sun showed a lone horseman on the trail above, coming down toward them at full gallop. A mutter ran along the column, with here and there the sharp click of a rifle being cocked. The rider drew closer without checking his speed and St. Vrain, in the lead, loosed a sudden joyous yell. "It's Charles! Charles Bent, and all in one piece!"

The reunion was warm and boisterous and heartfelt, but Dick sympathized with the noisy clamor that they keep going and "teach those varmints a lesson in manners they'll never forget." His feeling was one of letdown, of vengeance unsatisfied, blood unspilled.

Charles Bent raised his voice sharply against the growing war fever. "We stop here and turn back. Mexicans are a touchy and volatile people and when rumors start they tend to give way to emotions instead of reason. They've already regretted their impulsiveness and released all Americans with apologies. I was asked to ride out and stop you from rash actions, and I'm doing precisely that. We're turning back to Bent's Fort. Our private Mexican war is all over."

Later, trotting beside Dick on the trail back, he confided: "It was the news of your coming that did the trick. When the governor heard that an army of mountain men was on the way, he became positively green with fright. He begged me, practically on his knees, to turn you back. Now things will be quiet for a while. But the seeds of trouble are still there and sooner or later there'll be a bloody and terrible showdown. I'm only hoping that the people's personal confidence in Ceran and me will avert that showdown until our governments can work something out between them."

9

It was good to be back at Bent's Fort, to receive the unstinting praise of the partners for his successful trip, and to pocket a generous bonus for his profitable management.

Dick found things much the same, with one startling exception. Earlier in the spring William Bent had further cemented the firm's ties with the Cheyenne nation by formal marriage to the slim and beautiful Owl Woman, daughter of Gray Thunder, the respected keeper of the Cheyennes' sacred arrows. On one of his courting visits to the village on the South Platte, he had spied a splendid location forty miles north of present-day Denver, on a stream he named St. Vrain Creek. George Bent was already on the way with a trainload of equipment and a crew of Mexican workmen to build a smaller adobe counterpart of Bent's Fort, to be named Fort Lookout.

"What are your plans for the immediate future, Dick? You can go trading on your own, either from here or from the new post, or stay on with us."

"Thanks," Dick said. "I've had beaver on my mind ever since I came here, and seeing the streams full of them last winter only made it worse. I've been talking with the mountain men and a lot of them are willing to throw in with me for a season of trapping. Time a man reaches twenty-one like I just did, he starts to think about making a lot of money fast. Beaver's the fastest way I know without risking a big investment."

For the next few days he lazed around the fort, resting, renewing old friendships, and discussing his plans. It was pleasant enough, but there was an unfamiliar atmosphere of tension that was beginning to strain nerves.

The cause was a band of Pawnees who had been hanging around the neighborhood for weeks, sometimes swaggering in with professions of deep friendship, to trade or beg. These fierce predators of the Plains were hated and feared by all tribes as well as by the whites. Their hunting ground was above the North Platte but their marauding bands ranged from Canada to Mexico in search of scalps and plunder.

This band had never openly menaced the fort, but no one traveling alone or in a weak party was safe anywhere in the area. At least four travelers had been killed and a number of others chased almost to the gate. In consequence Bent's Fort was in a state of virtual siege. The tower watch was doubled, the gate kept closed and locked all day, and hunters went out only in parties of eight or ten. Even workmen building a new icehouse on the riverbank just beyond the wall kept their rifles handy and a watch posted.

Dick was outraged. "Why don't we take a few of the boys out and make good Indians out of the skunks?"

Holt, the fort storekeeper, shook his head bitterly. "The Bents are against it, as long as we aren't attacked here. They want to keep the strict neutrality they've maintained and avoid a Pawnee war that would scare away all their other trade. They keep hoping those devils will either go away or run into some Comanches who'll do the job for us. I suppose they're right, but it does go against the grain."

No one was more annoyed than a group of visitors, friends of the Bents from St. Louis, who had come out for the hunting. They were galled at not being able to dash out after game whenever the mood struck them, without waiting, as they had to do, for William to organize an armed escort. Dick went along on two such hunts and got to know them well.

His favorite was a fat and fun-loving prankster with the improbable name of Belshazar Dodd. Belzy Dodd wore a wig over a skull as bald as an egg. Dick treasured a hilarious memory-picture of Belzy jouncing across the prairie with his wig slipping down over his eyes. Between hunts, the fat man enlivened the fort with his stories and practical jokes.

Dick was strolling with Belzy one day when William came tramping across the *placita,* his face dark with anger. "Talk about pure gall! Eight of those Pawnee devils just rode up, bold as brass, claiming undying friendship and wanting to trade some ratty old skins for powder and shot. I wish I knew some way to get rid of them short of chasing them off and risking some bloody retaliation."

"Maybe I can do the trick for you, Will," Belzy said unexpectedly. "Come along and watch the fun."

William was dubious but finally led the pair out through the foot gate. The Pawnees were waiting patiently in the shade of the wall. They were smaller than the Cheyennes or Sioux, with sharp, cruel faces streaked with paint. Unlike the other Plains tribes, their heads were shaved except for a narrow strip over the crown that was thickened with paint and grease into a high, bristling crest.

"Wait here," Belzy whispered. He walked toward the Pawnees, glaring fiercely and muttering deep in his throat. Their pious smiles changed to expressions of alarm as the fat man circled them, breaking into a little shuffling dance step, accompanied by sharp barks. They shifted nervously backward as he halted suddenly, head thrust forward, twisting his moon face into a hideous scowl. Then, without warning, he loosed an earsplitting screech, snatched off his wig, and hurled it to the ground.

For a frozen moment the Pawnees were paralyzed. Then with howls of terror they fled down the river, yelling, dropping furs and blankets in blind panic. Belzy picked up the wig from the sand, dusted it against his knee, and fitted it back on his shining pate.

"I told you," he said, beaming. "I'll bet you a dollar to a fishhook they never come here to trade again."

William and Dick were clinging to one another, convulsed with laughter. "You win," William choked. "That one kept yelling 'White man scalps himself' all the way out of hearing."

It was indeed the last Pawnee trade visit but not the last of the Indians. Two mornings later the stock had just been driven from the corral to graze when the alarm bell set up its wild clangor and the voice of the watchman bawled, "Injuns! They're after the herd!"

Dick was just coming from breakfast. He ran for his rifle and reached the wall in time to see two mounted Pawnees splash across the Arkansas and vanish into the Mexican sandhills, driving a score or more of the fort's mules. The bodies of the two herders lay sprawled on the gravel, not fifty yards from the corral gate, bristling with arrows. Both had been scalped, their rifles taken.

By the time horses could be saddled and pursuit mounted the endless prairie wind had filled the Pawnee tracks with shifting sand. Most of the day was spent rounding up the scattered herd, burying the victims, and searching vainly for the Pawnees' trail. Anger was at white heat and there was no longer reason to forbid an attack. The problem now was to find the elusive Pawnees.

Dick, with Curdy and Wyler, ranged as far as the big timbers without finding fresh sign of the band. They were heading glumly back in late afternoon when a yelling rider overtook them. It was Wilson Mory, a scout from Captain Osborn's train which was due in any day from Independence. Mory was hatless and wild-eyed, his horse covered with lather.

"Dang Pawnee devils," he panted. "Jumped me at the Fork and chased me clean to the timbers. I bet my ears ring for a week from them Pawnee whistles."

"What about the train?" Dick cut in. "How come you're traveling alone?"

"They're follerin' a day or so behind, shorthanded and worried. We had to sign mostly green hands. Half of 'em are down sick and the other half ain't worth a hoot in a hurricane. Cap'n Osborn was afeared we'd be jumped at Pawnee Fork so I rid ahead to get help from the fort. The Pawnees are there, sure enough, jest layin' for the train."

"It's prob'ly the same pack that's been pesterin' us," Matt growled. "If the train's a day behind, we got time to round up the boys and get back to Pawnee Fork fust."

"What are we waiting for?" Dick barked and dug in his heels.

At the fort the clamorous crowd of volunteers was finally whittled down to Dick, Curdy, Wyler, and five others, all acknowledged crack shots and formidable fighters. After a few hours' sleep the eight set out at moonrise, riding hard to reach their destination as early in the day as possible, every man armed to the teeth and thirsting for vengeance.

As they pounded through the moonlit night, Dick's mind went back to his first Indian fight, which had taken place at that same Pawnee Fork crossing. The history of that bloody spot was one of almost incessant attacks. In the final tally, more white blood was spilled at Pawnee Fork than at any other place in the West.

The site of attacks was a point where the trail traversed a gloomy, rock-walled canyon whose stunted trees and masses of projecting or fallen rock gave perfect cover for an ambush. The column halted while Curdy went ahead to reconnoiter. He returned grinning.

"They're there, all right. I counted sixteen of the devils on foot and not a gun among 'em. They must know a train's coming because they're all so busy watching the trail from the east that they never noticed when I almost rode into 'em."

The encounter—short, sharp, and bloody—was too unequal to be called a fight. The column burst upon the startled Pawnees at a gallop, opening fire at extreme range. Five of the savages fell in the first volley. The survivors took shelter among the rocks and began arching arrows that fell short of their marks.

The frontiersmen remained in their saddles to reload, then

spread out to circle the spot, keeping just out of arrow range. When a Pawnee raised himself to draw his bow, a mountain rifle bellowed with deadly accuracy. Thirteen brown bodies were sprawled among the rocks when the three surviving Pawnees burst from cover and fled back through the pass, tossing away bows and arrows.

Dick's rifle jumped to his shoulder, the sights settling on a brown back. His finger was tightening on the trigger when he threw the barrel up, yelling, "Don't shoot! Hold your fire or you'll hit our boys! There's the train."

The first Bent wagons were rolling into view at the far end of the short canyon, with Captain Osborn and a handful of armed men riding cautiously in the lead. They reined in sharply, their horses rearing, as the three Pawnees with empty hands up, flung themselves down on the trail in token of surrender. They were cowering in the dust, covered by a half-dozen rifles, when Dick and his companions pounded up.

After exuberant greetings, Osborn pointed to the three terrified prisoners. "What should we do with these varmints?"

Someone shouted, "Make good Injuns out of the murdering skunks," and the cry was echoed from a score of throats. Dick threw his hands up high. "Hold on! I've got a better idea. If we finish them off, their friends won't know what happened. Pretty soon there'll be another pack of Pawnees nosing around to see what became of them. Then they'll start killing to even up the score and we'll have to do it all over."

"It makes sense," Wyler shouted. "Go on, Dick."

"I say give them food and send them back to their village to report what happened here. They can tell their people that if they give us any more trouble we'll take a big force and wipe out the whole Pawnee nation."

There was grumbling but cooler heads won the day and the captives were turned loose with provisions and a stern warning. Apparently the message and the bloody example made a deep impression, for thereafter Pawnee raiders gave Bent's Fort and the surrounding trails a wide berth.

Bent's Fort settled back into its accustomed routine, with friendly Indians coming to trade or visit, frontiersmen dropping by to gossip, and hunters resuming their former patterns. There was plenty of work for Dick but his mind was filled with dreams of a trapping fortune waiting in the mountains. He had planned to set out in the fall when beaver was in its prime and plews brought the top price.

Suddenly he was too impatient to wait out the dragging weeks. Summer furs brought less but he could still make more than by hanging around the fort. By fall they could be high in the mountains, the best streams located, and everything ready for a season of prosperity.

He discussed his idea and found seventeen veteran mountain men eager to join his brigade. Dan Wyler had engaged to guide a train back into Sioux country but Curdy was ready to follow Dick. At the last he got an unexpected break. Two trappers, Briggs and Burris, had married Snake Indian sisters and wanted to take them along to do the cooking and camp chores.

Dick was dubious about women on such a trek, but the old-timers reassured him. "You take 'em, boy, and you'll bless the day you did. A Snake squaw is clean, purty, quiet, and she'll make the best moccasins in the mountains. She can stand anything a man can, and more. It'll be money in your poke from the extry time they'll give you to tend your own plews."

Before such unassailable logic Dick yielded, and was never sorry. When they set out, the women's horses were loaded with pots, kettles, and ladles for cooking, along with extra deerskins and materials to repair or replace their garments. They also carried green coffee beans which they would scorch on a flat stone over the fire, then grind with a rounded stone. The coffee, together with sugar and tobacco, were the only provisions they carried. Flour was a luxury they could forego until their return. Wild game, eaten without salt, would be the only food they would know for eight to ten months. Even Dick had grown almost completely accustomed to meat without seasoning. If at rare times he felt a brief pang of salt-hunger, a pinch of gun-powder sprinkled on his meat made an adequate substitute.

Each man rode a sturdy Indian pony and led a string of pack-horses to carry his anticipated catch. Dick, like his companions, took only a minimum of essential supplies. They would be moving every day or two as an area was trapped out, and the less they had to haul the better.

One horse carried his trap-bag, a sack of heavy buffalo hide which could, in dire emergency, be boiled into soup. In the bag were his eight traps, each weighing five pounds with a chain weighing another three, spare trap springs and tools for making repairs. Another pack consisted of his buffalo sleeping robes, extra powder, a pig of Galena lead, and his bullet mold. On his own saddle his "possibles" bag held tobacco, spare flints, and a steel striker, repair parts for his rifle, sewing and mending sup-plies, and a rock-hard chunk of jerky for emergency rations.

With these and his wits, Dick expected to survive a fierce mountain winter and return in the spring a wealthy man.

10

THE fur brigade passed the mouth of Fountain Creek and began climbing, following the narrowing Arkansas up toward its headwaters among the tangled peaks of the Front Range. Trapping would not begin until they were in the high country. For the moment Dick had little to do but lounge in his saddle and enjoy the awesome grandeur of the mountain scenery. The trappers were in high spirits and the journey took on the aspect of a grand and unending picnic, with every meal a feast.

Buffalo were becoming more scarce as they left the Plains but there was no shortage of other meat. Elk, antelope, and the big-eared mule deer were fat and plentiful. Dick enjoyed his first bear steaks and roasts and was shortly introduced to the mountain man's delicacy—fat beaver tail, its leathery skin burned off in the fire and the inner meat boiled to melting tenderness.

He was promised an even finer treat when they reached mountain lion country. Matt Curdy told him, "You ain't et until you've et painter meat, Dick. It even puts fat cow in the shade and that takes some doin'."

The others nodded solemn agreement. Old Abel Ensley sighed reminiscently, "It do fer fair, Matt. But I fer one ain't belittlin' young horse or mule steaks. *Young* mule, mind ye, afore he gits old enough to be stringy and strong-tastin'."

Some of the men had brought along shotguns with a supply of light bird shot to conserve rifle balls. These contributed an endless supply of rabbit, squirrel, partridge, wild turkey, and prairie hen to the daily menu. The two Snake women were constantly jumping from their ponies to snatch up a few weeds or tufts of unusual grasses, or to grub up a strange root. With these they added wonderful and indescribable new flavors to the meats. The longer Dick traveled with the pair, the better he understood why men like William Bent and Kit Carson and Blackfoot Smith chose Indian wives. Not that he himself was interested in a wife, Indian or any other, nor did he intend to be for a long time to come.

At night Dick sat quietly by the fire and listened to the trappers' endless stories of experiences and adventures in the mountains until his mind was crammed with the lore of the trade. By the time they reached beaver country he had followed traps so often in imagination that he felt almost like a veteran himself.

They camped in a broad, open meadow ringed by towering mountains, not far below the famed Bayou Salade, or South Park. In every direction small, swift mountain streams tumbled down to find their way to the Arkansas. Where the gentler slope of the meadow tamed the tempestuous rush, the beaver had built their clever dams. Behind each a wide pond was dotted with the mud-and-stick domes of beaver houses.

Watching wide-eyed from a screening thicket, the men saw beaver that would easily top sixty pounds, whose plews would skin out to better than two pounds. Dick whistled softly. "If beaver prices'll stay up around seven dollars a pound this winter, we'll all go home rich."

"You aren't funnin' on that," Curdy agreed. "They's plews there will run fifteen dollars easy at prime." He sighed wistfully. "I sure wish we'd been here back in '33 when beaver was nine dollars a pound. Wouldn't *thet* have been some punkins?"

Except for a partnership arrangement between Burris and Briggs, each man was to run his set of traps by himself. Following a general direction selected by lot, he would work every likely pond and stream within a radius of eight to ten miles. Traps were set at dusk, when the beaver had gone to their houses for the night, and raised at dawn.

"You want I should go with you the fust time, Dick," Curdy asked, "to see you got the hang of it proper?"

"Thanks, Matt, but there's no need for you to lose out on your day's catch. I've picked up the general know-how listening to you fellows and the rest'll come by experience. I may as well go it alone right from the start and learn from my mistakes."

The sun was sliding behind the western mountains when they all shook hands and went their separate ways, leaving the Indian women in camp. Like the others, Dick carried his bag of heavy traps and his rifle, with powder horn, bullet pouch, and "possible" bag slung around his neck. In his belt were two pistols, his hatchet, and two knives, his heavy Green River and a lighter skinning knife, with his whetstone. Hung in front was a small, stoppered horn of castoreum, or beaver oil, whose musky, lingering stench covered the man-scent and lured beaver to the trap.

He moved with every sense alert to danger. They had seen no Indian sign but that was no assurance. This was country ranged by both Utes and Snakes, or Mountain Comanches. In addition, many of the fiercest Plains Indians came up in the late summer to hunt mule deer, or to cut lodgepoles and a special cedar used for bows. To any of these a lone trapper would be fair prey. Here, even more than on the open prairie, the price of survival was eternal vigilance.

Dusk was thickening over the meadow when Dick struck a small stream thick with beaver sign. The stumps of gnawed saplings stood like pale pickets in the gloom and the underbrush had been stripped clean of its lower branches. From upstream came the sound of water tumbling over a beaver dam.

He studied the bank, selecting the site of his first trap near a mud slide where beaver chuted into the stream. From his bag he took a trap with its five-foot chain and sprung the jaws until the trigger cocked. A float-stick was tied to the chain by a long cord. If the trap should be torn loose and dragged away, the floating stick would mark its location.

He waded in, gasping as the icy water knifed through his buckskins and then his hand as he splashed the bank to wash off the man-scent. The trap was carefully placed, the chain stretched toward midstream, and anchored with a stake pushed through the ring and deep into the sand bottom, to hold the trapped animal under until he drowned.

Last of all, Dick dipped the end of a long willow twig into the foul-smelling castoreum and stuck it to hang just above the water over the trap. The beaver, lured by the scent, would step on the pan as he stood up to reach the twig.

Some yards upstream Dick waded out, washing his scent off the bank, and moved on. He set his second trap in a quiet eddy below the beaver dam, his third in the pond above. By the time the last was placed it was pitch dark and his hands and feet were numb from the cold water. If it was agony now, in summer, what would it be when cold weather struck? Dick pushed the picture from his mind, set his teeth to still their chattering, and turned back to camp.

Most of the others were already back, the fire blazing and coffee hot. Curdy greeted him with a tired grin. "How did you make out, hoss?"

"I'll tell you better when I lift the traps," Dick said. "Beaver's there aplenty. If I don't get my share, it won't be their fault."

"You'll get it," Curdy said confidently. "Like Dan allus said, you got a streak o' borned luck froze to you."

Dawn was just paling the eastern sky when Dick rolled out of his robes, groaning. His legs were cramped, his buckskins shrunken and board-stiff from the soaking and fire-drying. The others were stumbling in circles, pulling their knees up high, then slapping their moccasins down hard to stir the blood and loosen stiff joints and muscles.

A gulp or two of hot coffee and they were off to retrace their sets and lift the traps. Dick jogged through the dawn-gloom, his mind torn between doubt and hope. His spirits took a sickening plunge when his first trap came up empty. They shot up again when the second yielded a fifty-pound beaver, the wet fur sleek and glistening, as fine as any man could ask of a summer plew.

He skinned it on the bank, his hands making slow work of the unfamiliar task but doing it carefully. He cut out the scent gland for its castoreum, took the tail for cooking, and went on, feeling lighthearted and optimistic again.

His eight traps yielded five plews, a fine catch even if one was a kitten, worth only a dollar or two. It was, Curdy told him back at camp, further proof of the Wootton luck. He himself had four and counted it a good night's trapping.

The rest of the day was spent in "graining" the skins—scraping every shred of flesh away—then stretching them on willow hoops for drying. By common consent they decided to stay over for one more set of traps. Now that the beaver were alerted it would be useless to try the same waters again, but further upstream the ponds were still virgin. Although Dick took only four plews, he was gratified at the improvement in his dexterity and speed.

The brigade moved on, the days falling into a pattern that varied only rarely, the bundles on their packhorses growing steadily bulkier and heavier until they had to construct a press and make them into hundred-pound bales. They cut away from the Arkansas and crossed the Sawatch Range over Poncha Pass, turning due south toward the San Juans and the Continental Divide.

The first hard frosts of fall caught them working the headwaters of the Rio Grande del Norte. Now almost from day to day they could see the beavers' fur grow thicker and glossier and more valuable as it reached its fall prime. They swung north again, up through Colorado, moving camp every day as they raced the oncoming winter.

They had encountered no Indians and suffered only minor harassments, though one of these could have had serious consequences. Taking up his set one morning, Dick found the last one missing. He searched the water vainly for a sight of the float-stick.

Then, on the far bank of the pond, he saw the dirt freshly gouged below a clump of willows that had been threshed and flattened. He guessed what had happened even before he saw the paw-prints of a giant grizzly bear, with one showing the clear imprint of the missing trap. The bear had blundered over the set, perhaps drawn by the beaver scent, and been caught by a forepaw.

Dick dropped his trap bag and grimly checked the priming of his rifle. He wanted the bearskin, he wanted bear meat and, most of all, he wanted the trap and chain which represented a twenty-four-dollar debt on the Bent & St. Vrain books. It represented a vastly greater loss in plews.

The trail was fresh and easy to follow. Every few yards the earth was gouged and scuffed where the bear had tried vainly to beat off the stubborn jaws of the trap. A half mile or so back from the pond he spied the great shaggy monster, lumbering at an awkward gallop, stopping frequently to hammer the trap on the ground and tear at it with his teeth. It was the first grizzly he had ever seen close up and excitement made him hasty and incautious.

He fired, aiming for the neck joint, but instead of dropping, the bear whirled, roaring and snapping at the side of its body. Suddenly it spied Dick and started toward him in a lumbering charge, snarling fiercely, the trap chain clattering and whipping. Dick was on one knee, reloading in frantic haste, trying to estimate a double powder charge.

He rammed the ball home and jerked out his wiping stick as the bear reared up on hind legs for its lunge, forepaws wide to sweep him into its crushing embrace. There was no time to aim. The rifle flew up and crashed. The tremendous kick of its extra charge drove the butt into Dick's shoulder with a sledgehammer impact that spun him half around and sent him sprawling backward.

The slug caught the bear full in the throat. For a moment it stood rigid, a full seven feet of halted fury, and then crashed down, the great head flopping on the shattered neck. Dick got up, panting, and reloaded with hands that were not quite steady before cautiously examining his kill.

It was obvious at once that the gigantic hide alone would be too heavy to pack on his back. He whirled and set off for camp at a run to get help and a packhorse.

Curdy, Briggs, and Burris were the only men there when he burst in with his story. "Help me unload one of my pack-horses and get back there before wolves get at the carcass."

"Not your hosses," Curdy snapped, spinning around. "If they ain't used to bear, they'll bolt and run at the first smell. I got one that's toted bear hide before. She don't like it none but she won't kick the tallow out of ever'body to get away." As he ran for his string he flung over his shoulder, "And don't worry none about your hide gettin' chawn up, Dick. There ain't a varmint in the mountains, savin' only dang fool men, who'll go near a grizzly, dead or alive."

Getting the enormous hide rough-dressed and prepared for packing cost them an extra day, but to Dick the magnificent trophy was worth the delay. It took several days of strain and struggle before the horses grew sufficiently used to the smell of the bear hide to be manageable on the trail.

By the time the train had settled back to normal travel, the first light snow had powdered the ground and the streams were edged with thickening ice. They were beyond the Uintahs and following the Green River into the Wyoming hills. One morning Dick looked at the gray sky and felt the stinging bite of the north wind in his nostrils and came to a reluctant de-cision.

"I know we're all froze to get a few more plews, but I'd say we've about used up our time. Matt says the bears have already holed up for the winter and I'd hate to think a bear was smarter than me."

Curdy grinned approvingly. "They's two things allus goes to-gether, Dick. One is *gettin'* the beaver. T'other is gettin' back alive to spend it. I'm thinkin' we better find us our hole and find it mighty quick, hoss."

II

THEY wintered in Wyoming, at the head of a sheltered canyon on the rim of Bridger Basin. Despite the blizzards and the bitter cold, it was a time of comparative ease and plenty after the rigors of trapping. Herds of deer, elk, antelope, and even buffalo had drifted into the valleys and canyons for refuge from the storms. Whenever the weather broke, the men tramped out on homemade snowshoes and shot all the meat they could pack.

Almost before the ice broke up in the spring they were out again, for spring plews commanded the peak of premium prices. They worked back down the Green River, making wide swings to avoid country already trapped out by previous brigades. At its mouth they turned northeast up the Grand River, later renamed the Colorado. It was here that their phenomenal luck began to run thin.

The men had fanned out as usual at the crack of dawn to raise their sets, returning late in the morning with their traps and plews. Dick had been busy at the graining block for more than an hour when a sudden realization made him straighten and stare around the camp.

"Wait a minute," he said sharply. "Abel Ensley and Frenchy Ladue haven't come back from their sets and they're usually among the first ones in. Did anybody see them this morning?"

There were startled looks and a chorus of noes. One by one the men laid down their graining knives and stood up, looking at each other with troubled eyes. The missing men were both veteran trappers with years of mountain experience. That either could lose his way or wander off was unthinkable. The same fear stood naked in every eye. *Indians!*

"Anybody know where they set their traps last night?"

Curdy snorted. "Them two old roosters was so tight-mouth they wouldn't tell their own mother where the Missoury River is. As I recollect, Abel drawed a course due west toward that jaggedy peak and Frenchy's line was a mite to the southwest."

Dick's jaw set. "We'll split up. Matt, you and your bunch try to back trail Frenchy while the rest of us look for Abel. Keep your priming fresh and your eyes peeled for redskins."

A full day of searching brought no trace of the missing men nor a clue to their disappearance. They found no sign of hostiles but Curdy gloomily insisted they were about. "You kin hee-haw me if you wants to, but this hoss can *smell* Injun."

They posted night guards but there was no alarm. Nevertheless they maintained extra vigilance as they worked on upriver. Nothing happened until they reached the mouth of Piny Creek. That morning they all had good catches. They were busy at their graining when Curdy glanced up and said quietly, "Thar's your Snakes."

The Indians were across the stream, sitting quietly on their ponies, watching the camp. Dick estimated sixty or more in full war regalia, shields freshly painted, bright feathers fluttering from their lances. Dick dropped his knife to reach for his rifle.

"Easy, hoss," Curdy said softly. "They's time enough to make fight moves when they start something. I figger they're lookin' us over now, makin' up their minds are we easy pickin's or bad medicine. Lookin' into the wrong end o' trappers' guns ain't a thing they want to be hasty about."

"Maybe our two Snake squaws can parley them into letting us alone."

Curdy shook his head. "Nope. These two come from beyont the Divide, while them over there are likely from Iron Belly's bunch, which ain't friendly to the rest. Besides, once they're froze to get our hosses and plews and scalps, there ain't *no* female kin talk 'em out of it. Only guns kin do that."

After what seemed an eternity, the Indians turned and rode leisurely up the stream and out of sight. Curdy sprang to his feet. "Now's the time to move, and lively, hoss. Bring all the animals in and fore-hopple, so's they can't be stampeded. Then start draggin' up logs or rocks or anything to git behind."

No traps were set that evening. They ate early and put out the fire before dark to prevent being targeted by its glow. Then, taking turns at watch, they sweated out a quiet night. The next day they stayed in camp, never more than an arm's length away from their rifles.

Late in the afternoon the Indians appeared again, riding a leisurely circle completely around the camp just beyond rifle range. Again the night passed without alarm, but in the morning there were moccasin tracks almost up to the barricades. Everyone was getting edgy from strain and uncertainty.

"Why don't they jump us if they're going to?" Dick exploded. "If we sit here much longer the season for spring plews will be gone. I say we break camp today and move on upriver. If we keep going, they may give up and go on about their business."

"It's wuth a try," Buck McNeil agreed. "And we can keep an eye out for a stronger place to fort up, come night. I ain't too happy with this'n, I'll tell you."

The new campsite they found was infinitely more defensible but the next morning revealed moccasin prints circling it in considerable numbers, though the guards had heard no sound. They moved on, picking another strongpoint for the night. The Indians were still unseen, following and watching the brigade.

"You know," Dick said thoughtfully, "I've got an idea of what's keepin' them off. When we put out the fire at night it's so dark they can't see whether we're awake or asleep, or where the sentries are. They're waiting to make sure they can catch us completely off guard."

"Could be," Curdy agreed. "They might be waitin' fer a moonlight night to see by. On the other hand, they could be just pushin' us toward some likely spot for ambush, or mebbe they've sent for extry help to make sure we go under."

On this cheering thought they settled down for another nerve-racking night. The night wind held a spring softness and Dick fell asleep thinking of beaver shedding their silky winter fur and shedding with it the extra dollars the plew might have brought.

The next night they camped at the edge of a small grove of cottonwoods. As usual, they dined early and had the last embers of the cookfire buried by dusk. Afterward, they sat for a time discussing defense strategies in low voices before turning into their buffalo robes. Before he fell asleep, Dick studied the sliver of rising moon and estimated that in four to five days at most there would be sufficient light for a night attack.

It came, instead, with the first light of the next morning. Dick had just finished his predawn two-hour watch and was dozing off. He had lain for a time watching the morning catch fire, seeing the limbs and branches and leaves of the cottonwoods lose their blur and sharpen to black silhouettes against the sky, lacing the rose sunrise with pattern.

His eyelids were growing heavy when suddenly a flash of gunflame lit the dawn gloom. A rifle sent its flat, smashing thunder against the circling mountains and the voice of the new watch bawled, "Injuns! Injuns!"

He was up instantly, rifle ready, falling back among the great silver trunks of the cottonwoods. All around him the shadowy figures of the other trappers were running to positions behind the trees, positions decided upon in the quiet talk of the previous night. From back in the grove he heard the soft snorting of the horses, silently moved there in the black of night as an added precaution.

The sentries were dropping back, yelling and cursing and stumbling as if just awakened from heavy sleep, making noise enough for the whole brigade. Beyond them, in the gray half-light, Dick could make out the shadow shapes of the Snakes.

They had left their ponies behind and were charging on foot in a loose, curving line meant to fold around the camp in a pincers to cut off any escape. The charge had been carried on in un-Indian silence until the moment of the sentry's yells and shot. Then an unearthly howling broke out, and there was the twang of bowstrings and the eerie whisper of arrows.

Most of the arrows arched down among the abandoned sleeping robes but a few thudded into the tree trunks beyond. Dick leaned around his sheltering tree, brought his rifle barrel down toward the bounding shapes, and fired. One of the shapes tumbled in a loose heap, and then other guns were banging from the grove, and more figures were falling.

The line wavered, broke, and fell back. The light was growing swiftly now and it was possible to make out the figures of Indians, running in pairs, dragging their dead or wounded. At one side an Indian stumbled away, bent double. Another hunched along the ground, pulling useless legs, until comrades seized him by the arms and hauled him away.

Beyond rifle range the Snakes gathered in a milling mass, yelling their rage and frustration. Above this tumult a single voice rose and fell in a high, shrill chanting.

"They'll try onct more, I'm thinking," Matt Curdy said from behind a nearby tree, "But their hearts ain't rightly in it. That singin'll be a medicine man fixin' a spell to make 'em all bullet-proof or some such foolishment."

The Indians came again in a screeching rush. A handful of old fusils banged and swarms of arrows whispered and thudded in the grove. Dick heard a yelp and a stream of swearing from close by his cover. One of the trappers had been hit but not too badly, to judge by the lurid commentary.

Then the brigade was firing and reloading and firing again with cool speed. Gaps opened in the charging line. The attack faltered, lost momentum, and broke into wild retreat, the Indians carrying off their dead and wounded. This time there was no re-assembling beyond gun range. The fleeing mob streamed up over a distant ridge and vanished from view.

"We're shet o' them fer good, I'd say," Curdy remarked,

stepping from behind his tree. He chuckled. "Dogged if I wouldn't hate to be in that medicine man's moccasins about now."

A man named Batcher had a Snake arrow through the flesh of his upper arm. They broke the shaft and pulled it out, binding the wound with a piece of beaver skin. This was their only casualty. It was generally agreed that the Indian losses could be no less than twenty dead and a number wounded.

It was a complete and smashing victory and one with lasting effects. The next time Dick entered their country the Snakes hurriedly sent a delegation bearing presents and assurances of friendship. Peace was established and never again was Cut-Hand or any of his party bothered by that tribe.

They reached Bent's Fort in late March of 1838, almost nine months to the day from the time of their departure. Trapping had been reluctantly abandoned because the packhorses could carry no more plews. Dick found he had become almost a legend. To have commanded an expedition over so much ground and for so long a time with the loss of only two men was almost a miracle.

When he had paid all costs, Dick found himself with over four thousand dollars in net profit for his share of the peltry. It was more money than he had ever possessed in his life, more than he had even dared hope for from his first season of trapping.

He found letters from his parents waiting for him at the fort. There was no word of reproach for his staying away so long, but behind the lines he could read a wistful loneliness that put a lump in his throat. For the first time he felt a nostalgia for the rolling hills and green fields of home and a longing to see his mother and dad again. That night he lay awake for long hours and in the morning his decision was made. He went to William Bent.

"I guess I've got to head home. I've been promising my folks to come for two years now, as soon as I made my stake. Now I've got no excuse for keeping them waiting any longer."

"All right, Dick. There's a train leaving for the East in a few days and I'd be glad to have you go along as guard. We'll miss you here. There'll always be a job, in case the prairie fever gets to tugging too hard."

A few days later Dick rode out through the gate toward the sunrise with his throat tight and a dull ache in his heart. He looked back only once and briefly, for fear his resolve would weaken.

The destination of the train was Westport, Missouri, the booming new town that had stolen the Santa Fe trade from Independence. Here he could take a steamer to one of the Illinois ports across the river from St. Louis and walk from there to his home.

His thoughts broke off sharply and he chuckled aloud. For a moment he had forgotten that he was now a man of wealth and modest fame. "Walk—blazes! I'll buy me the finest piece of horseflesh in Illinois and ride home in style."

A few weeks later Dick rode through the gate of Bent's Fort and dismounted in the *placita,* amid wild whoops of welcome. William Bent hurried over to pump his hand, his look quizzical.

"How were your parents, Dick? I trust you found them in good health."

Dick grinned sheepishly. "Aw, you know, I never got further than Westport. All those crowds of people rushing around and jostling and hollering, they got on my nerves. Then I saw how much money it cost just to eat and sleep and buy some city duds and my little pile started looking mighty puny. I decided the thing to do was spend a couple more years in the mountains and go back to Kentucky with a real stake, enough to live on in comfort. I hung around a few days to see the elephant and then I bought me a horse and headed back for home." He paused, savoring the word. "Yes, sir. Back here to home."

12

In September, with eighteen other men, Dick set out on what was destined to be the longest trapping expedition in the history of the American frontier. Before it ended he would explore thousands of miles of wilderness no white man's eye had ever before seen, far in advance of Fremont's later widely acclaimed "discoveries."

Dan Wyler was somewhere up in the Sioux nation, trading out of the new Fort Lookout, but Curdy was one of the first to sign on with Dick. Besides some noted French-Canadian mountain men, the brigade also included four Arapaho and three Shawnee Indians, all experienced trappers. Their supplies were as rudimentary as the previous winter, but in greater quantity and carried on longer strings of packhorses.

This time, from the headwaters of the Arkansas they continued west to the Green, following that river to its source high in the mountains of Wyoming. Working north, they followed the Big Horn to its juncture with the Yellowstone and turned west across present-day Montana and Idaho, trapping the Snake and Salmon rivers.

A few days out of Bent's Fort two of the men fell to arguing about the date. A search of packs and possibles bags disclosed that no one had remembered to bring an almanac, which would have enabled them to use the phases of the moon as an accurate calendar.

"We ought to keep some kind of check of time," Dick said. "After a few months the days'll get so tangled up in our minds that we won't know whether we ought to be getting ready for summer or winter."

As a rough-and-ready substitute calendar, they squared up a stout, seasoned stick, cutting tiny notches on one edge for every day since they had left the fort. This was entrusted to the keeping of old Gus Charlefou, who was to add a fresh notch each morning thereafter as a record of the days. By the time they reached the Columbia River, two edges of the stick were a mass of notches which no one felt ambitious enough to count.

In that time they had had only one serious mishap. Although it came from the hands of Snake Indians, it was not actually a breach of faith on the part of that nation, which had treated them with wary courtesy. The man responsible, and also the victim, was August Claymore, the oldest trapper in the mountains.

Claymore was an obstreperous old rooster at best and his attitude toward all Indians was anything but diplomatic. Returning from his traps one morning, he encountered a party of young Snake warriors with a horse that caught his eye. In his usual arrogant manner, Claymore demanded that they trade it to him for one of his plews.

An argument flared and Claymore reached for his rifle. The alarmed Indians swung their war clubs and knocked him down, then began beating him on the head until his skull was crushed. They were about to scalp him when Dick and Matt Curdy appeared, drawn by the old man's yells. The Snakes leaped onto their ponies and fled.

Old Claymore lay motionless, drenched in blood. Above his closed eyes a jagged piece of broken skull protruded from a wide gash. Curdy stared at the figure and shook his head. "Poor old cuss! With his disposition, some Injun was bound to do fer him, sooner or later. You reckon we ought to lug his corpse clean back to camp, or get the rest of the boys and bury him proper right here, Dick?"

At that moment Claymore gave a bubbling sigh and his

83

hands twitched feebly. "Lord a'mighty, he's still alive, Matt. Even if he can't last long, the only decent thing is to patch him up enough so his brains won't leak out and get him to camp to die proper on his own robes."

They pushed the broken bone back into place, stitched the skin back with deer sinew and carried the gaunt figure back to camp. While they waited for him to finish his dying, the trappers occupied themselves by scooping out a shallow grave and lugging up rocks to pile over it as protection against wolves. One of the Frenchmen had packed a woolen suit along for some possibly festive occasion. In a burst of generosity, he donated this for Claymore's burial suit.

The day dragged on with no change in Claymore's condition. They finally rolled into their sleeping robes, planning on a dawn burial and an early start. In the morning, when they pulled back the robe to remove the corpse, Claymore opened his eyes and swore at them in a weak whisper for not bringing him coffee.

Not only did Claymore confound them by recovering completely but with his old belligerence he flatly refused to return the donated burial suit. Years later, when he was the last mountain man still trapping for a living, he wore it on special occasions.

Along the Columbia they faced the bitter fact that they had already gotten all the plews their horses could possibly pack. The only solution was to turn northward to the British Canadian fur post at Vancouver and dispose of part of their load there.

Despite a growing quarrel over the boundary between the United States and Canada, they were received with courtesy. They were not too happy with the prices but they sold enough peltry to lighten the loads. Then they turned southward, trapping along the Pacific slope of the Rockies. They were in the shadow of Mount Rainier when a double disaster struck the brigade.

Old Charlefou was then riding a fine Nez Percé (the mountain men pronounced it Nepercy) horse to his traps. Returning to camp one morning he was jumped by a war party of Blackfeet on the prowl for scalps and plunder. Their ponies were no match for the powerful Nez Percé but they doggedly gave chase.

Well beyond range of their arrows, old Charlefou could not resist turning around to thumb his nose at the disgruntled pursuers. When he faced front again, his mount was almost on the rim of a deep, narrow chasm, a gash opened across the plateau by some early cataclysm of nature. His horse was already too near the edge to stop and running too fast to turn. Charlefou took the only possible alternative and drove in his spurs. His horse made a magnificent leap, but the gash was too wide, and mount and rider crashed to the bottom. The horse was instantly killed and Charlefou, knocked unconscious and with both legs broken, was pinned under the carcass.

The Blackfeet rode up and down the chasm but could find no easy way down to take the scalp and finally rode off in disgust. Charlefou regained consciousness presently, but was unable to drag his smashed legs free. He still had his rifle, but he was afraid to fire signal shots for fear the Indians were still close by.

Meanwhile, when he failed to return to camp, the whole brigade set out to search for him. No one knew exactly where he had been so they missed the trail and hunted in vain until dark.

At the first light of day they set out again. By that time Charlefou, suffering from thirst and hunger and the agony of his broken legs, had thrown caution to the winds and begun firing his rifle. Dick and a group of trappers heard the shots faintly and finally located their source. It took the remainder of the day to rig a sling of picket ropes and lower Dick to free the injured man and drag him out.

They set and splinted the broken legs as best they could by the light of their campfire. The next day they moved on, Charlefou riding in a sling between two of the packhorses. Two months later he was up and running his traps with the best of them.

The accident, however, brought a sharp change in the feelings of the old Frenchman. Until that time he had been an ardent friend of all Indians, frequently lecturing the rest of the brigade on their suspicious attitude toward the red man.

"Ze Indian ees a human being," he would protest. "Treat heem as one, weeth kindness and understanding, and he weel return zat kindness to you."

"Maybe that'll work with Cheyennes," Dick told him during one of the frequent debates. "They're the decentest of all. But I wouldn't trust one of the others behind my back."

Following his near-fatal disaster, Charlefou became the most rabid Indian hater of the brigade. Years later, on jury duty in Taos at the trial of an Indian charged with killing a white man, he was awakened and asked his verdict. Although he had slept through the entire testimony, the old man roared, "Why, hang him, of course! He's Injun, ain't he? If he ain't guilty yet, he will be sooner or later."

The second part of the double disaster was not discovered for some time. A question as to the date arose and was referred to Charlefou. He started to rummage in his pack and then stopped. "Fellers, I just recollect. When I fell into that gap, the stick jounced outa my bag. As fur as I know, it's still there."

The only full-scale Indian fight of the whole journey was an all-out major battle, by far the most fierce and most prolonged Dick had experienced. They had frequently seen small bands of Indians who followed the brigade for a day or two and then disappeared, obviously unwilling to tangle with so grimly competent a crew.

Then one day they rode over a rise and came face to face with a whole village of Indians on the move. Dick estimated at least a hundred warriors escorting a long column of women and children and old people, dragging their lodges and personal possessions on dog and pony travois. There were some tense moments as the trappers cocked their rifles, determined to sell their lives at the highest possible price.

Then a handful of older men rode out, holding up their

empty hands and asking for parley. Dick tried to converse by signs but had to admit defeat on many details. He told Curdy helplessly, "They say they're friendly but I'm dogged if I can make out what tribe they are from their signs or paint marks."

"I know," Curdy said. "They're a small tribe, relatives of the Utes. Some calls 'em Moachi and some Muache, and I've even heerd 'em called Monarchs by some. This here is the village of a chief called Sitting Buffalo. They ain't usually as all-out fierce as their cousins, but they'll steal your last plew and then lift your scalp from behind if you go lookin' fer it."

They smoked the pipe and exchanged presents, Dick reluctantly parting with a couple of sticks of tobacco and a handful of coffee in exchange for a ratty blanket and some mangy skins. The parting was a relief, but a short-lived one. When they camped that night, the Indians suddenly appeared, setting up their skin lodges less than a mile away. Despite double guards that night, a small pack of plews was missing in the morning.

Thereafter the Indians followed them day by day, camping close each night. And each night the trappers lost some other small but irritating item. When they protested, the Indian emissaries came promptly with shabby gifts and voluble expressions of enduring friendship. It became increasingly obvious that the brigade was having both its strength and its patience tested in preparation for an eventual showdown.

Efforts to shake off or discourage their unwanted shadows were futile. It became necessary to leave a guard at camp to protect their property while the others were out on their traplines.

Nevertheless, they came in from the set one morning to find three horses missing. These were the property of a Shawnee trapper named Hawk-Flying-Into-The-Sun, and the theft constituted a final straw to human endurance. When Hawk came back from inspecting his cavyard, swearing in Shawnee and mangled English, Dick reached for his saddle and apishamore—the softly tanned elkskin saddle blanket.

"They've been froze to see how far they can push us," he

snapped, "and I guess this is about the limit. Anybody who's of the same mind can come along and welcome."

The whole brigade rode grimly to the village. The stolen horses were grazing with the Indian pony herd, an open challenge too plain to be ignored. With the young Moachi horse-watchers sullenly looking on, they cut out the Shawnee mounts and herded them back to camp.

They had barely hazed the trio back into the corral with their other horses when a dozen mounted Indians appeared, charging down in a brazen effort to stampede the herd. An impatient rifle banged and the leading warrior slid from his pony. A moment later the entire Moachi warrior force swept into view in a howling charge.

The trappers were old hands at the business and not to be panicked by an overwhelming superiority of numbers. Following long-established rote, they broke into pairs, each pair springing to preplanned cover. As one fired, he dropped back to reload and his companion sprang into his place with gun ready.

The Indians, who had hoped to catch all the trappers with guns emptied at the same time, were caught by the withering fire and driven back, lugging their casualties. There was never a moment's letup in the steady hail of death, one reloading as the other fired with a smooth and unhurried precision that presented an almost unbroken sheet of fire to the attackers. In the face of that fearful destruction the Indians broke and retreated toward their village, howling their rage and frustration.

Dick sprang from his cover. "Come on, boys! Now is the time to settle this once and for all."

With a ragged cheer the trappers surged out to chase the fleeing foe, dropping to a knee to fire, then reloading on the run and shooting again. The retreating Indians fled through their village and out again in wild panic. The trappers, following on their heels, ran along the littered streets, pulling and hauling the lodges down. They stopped only when the last Moachi had vanished from sight and the village was a shambles of overturned lodges, some of them burning from abandoned fires.

Dusk was closing in when the victors returned to camp. It had been a smashing victory but a costly one. Three trappers were buried at dawn, the graves packed with rocks to keep off wolves. Afterward the packhorses were led back and forth over the top to obliterate traces so that the Indians could not scalp the bodies for revenge.

About noon three Indians appeared, waving a dirty white rag on a pole, a symbol they had evidently adopted from some previous conflict with whites. At their head was a doddering old patriarch named Lone Wolf who, Dick suspected dryly, was the most expendable member of the tribe.

"The whites have beaten us," the old man quavered. "We have lost many young men and our village, and now we wish only to be friends. We will fight no more if the white men will let us come and rebuild our lodges and bury our dead."

They smoked the peace pipe and thereafter saw no more of the troublesome foe. The brigade moved on, seeing country no man of their race had ever before beheld.

They were awed by the majesty of the great redwood forests and stunned by the giant sequoias. Crossing into Mexican California they swung west and got their first sight of the blue Pacific near the old Spanish mission of San Luis Obispo.

The streams of California were swarming with beaver but in that equable climate the fur was thin and poor. One morning Dick threw his catch down in disgust. "These ratty plews aren't worth the trouble of scraping. I'm for packing away the traps and heading back to Bent's Fort."

There was unanimous agreement and with no great urgency to drive them, they turned the remainder of the journey into a grand sightseeing tour. They spent some time along the lower Colorado River, then followed the Gila up across what is now Arizona and Utah, stopping here and there to trap but finding the fur almost uniformly poor in grade.

One day they encountered a band of Mexican traders on their way home from an expedition to the Snakes. Dick knew several of them from visits to Bent's Fort and made a deal for them to take part of his furs to Taos, to be picked up after his return.

They were now crossing the harsh, barren desert country of the Pah-Ute Indians and once more they moved with every sense doubly sharp and the shadow of death riding constantly at their shoulders.

The Pah-Utes were generally considered the most savage and barbarous of all tribes. They were not only cannibals by choice but almost the only tribe to poison their arrows and lances. The method was to tie a fresh deer or buffalo liver on the end of a stick and poke it into a rattlesnake den to be struck repeatedly by the angry snakes. When thoroughly soaked with the venom, the meat was put away to rot. Arrows and spearpoints were poked into the putrefied mass and left until coated with the poison. Before their journey ended, Dick became intimately acquainted with these customs.

They were following a winding mountain trail one day when Pierre Le Bonte's riding horse went lame. He swung out of the column, shouting, "She 'ave no doubt a sharp stone in the frog. Go along and I will catch up when I have removed it."

They plodded on a full mile before Dick threw up his hand to halt the brigade. "Le Bonte should have caught up with us before now. Everybody stay here and keep a sharp watch while I go back and see what's keeping him."

"Not all alone you don't, hoss," Curdy said sharply. "Not in Pah-Ute country. I'm going with you."

They found what was left of Le Bonte without difficulty, and immediately afterward Dick went off to the side of the trail and was sick. There was no need to dig the grave very deeply, or to worry about scavenging wolves.

A few evenings later they were sitting around the supper fire when the evening quiet was suddenly broken by the twang of bowstrings and a flight of arrows showered down on them. They all jumped up and raced out, cocking their rifles, in time to see a small band of Indians burst from a thicket and race off out of sight in the dusk. They got off a few angry shots that did no visible damage and returned to their supper, swearing.

The only casualty was another French-Canadian, Antoine Le Duc, who had sustained an arrow gash along his left arm. They dressed the cut, teasing Le Duc about his horrible wound, and turned in for the night. They were awakened shortly before dawn by the Frenchman's screams. Only when they saw the great black bulging mass that had been an arm did they realize the arrow had borne the fatal poison.

There was nothing at all they could do. All the rest of his life Dick's dreams would be haunted by the agonized screams of Le Duc during the twenty-four hours it took him to die from the Pah-Ute poison.

Since the loss of their calendar stick they had occasionally hazarded wild guesses at the date or season. The unvarying climate of southern California threw them completely out of balance. Dick finally suggested they make up a pool and guess the time of their eventual arrival back at Bent's Fort.

When they finally arrived, after almost two years and five thousand miles of wandering, the nearest guess was more than a month off. It was midsummer of 1840 when they rode in and vast changes had taken place during their long absence.

They got back just in time for a fantastic spectacle. Years of earnest effort by the Bents had finally resulted in a great peace conference of warring southern tribes. All up and down both sides, the Arkansas River was lined with villages of erstwhile enemies, now in a frenzy of feasting each other and vowing eternal peace.

Dick was wandering through the massed villages when he suddenly heard a familiar voice yelling, "Dick! Dick Wootton, for the love of heaven, get me out of this."

He whirled, seeing at first only a Comanche in his customary habiliments of a warrior. Then he saw an open, freckled, sunburned face and recognition burst on him.

"*Jim!* Jim Hobbs! But . . . but I thought we lost you way

back on the trail that day you and John Baptiste ran off chasing your buffalo."

"We figgered so too," Jim told him, clutching Dick's hand. "But the chief took a shine to both of us and made us his sons, sort of. I finally had to marry old Wolf's daughter and we got a son three years old, but I still ain't no Injun and both me and John want out. For pity's sake, see can you buy us out of this and quick."

Dick rushed to the Bents, who arranged a conference. Both boys were finally ransomed, Jim Hobbs by payment of six yards of red flannel, a pound of tobacco, and an ounce of beads. John Baptiste, who had not made so deep an impression, was let go for one aging mule. The Cheyennes and Arapahoes wound up a week of feasting and dancing and exchanging of gifts vowing eternal friendship with their ancient enemies, the Comanches, Kiowas, and Prairie Apaches. The peace might not last, but for the moment it brought a fantastic boom to Bent & St. Vrain trade.

The tribes finally scattered to make meat and the affairs of the fort drifted slowly back to normalcy. In the late fall Dick and Curdy rode down to Taos in New Mexico, to pick up the peltry he had sent there by the Mexican traders. This would be his first visit and Dick looked forward with eager interest to seeing the Mecca of every mountain man, his dream of royal and rowdy entertainment.

13

"Taos," Curdy said, pronouncing it Touse, "is ever'thing, and again it's nothin'. When you come down to it, we ain't exactly goin' to Taos at all, which is a mizzable little Injun village over at the foot of yonder mountain. This here is the Valley of Taos. We're headin' fer the Mex settlement o' San Fernandez where the Bents' store is and where the boys shine at the fandangos."

"I swear," Dick said, "the more I hear about a fandango the more unsure I am whether it means a big dance or a big fight."

"Why," Curdy said solemnly, "it's both. The dancin's the meat of it and the fightin's the seasoning that makes it tasty. But you'll see fer yourself tonight, like enough."

"Not me, Matt. I never danced in my life and don't even know how."

"It don't take knowin'. You jest grab a purty Mex girl and start swingin' her around and stompin' your feet and whooping, and that's all there is to the dancin' part. By'n by her Mex feller pulls a big knife and tries to take her away, an' that's when a fandango really gets lively."

Dick laughed and turned his attention back to the strange, foreign landscape of El Valle de Taos. Coming over Sangre de Cristo Pass they had shivered in an icy north wind that whipped clouds of fresh-fallen snow across their trail. Here the sun was hot on their backs and the little fields that dotted the valley, separated by irrigation ditches, were bright green.

They skirted a flock of grazing sheep and overtook a long string of Mexican burros, looking like walking brush piles under

93

enormous loads of pine fagots gathered in the mountains. Beside the tiny animals, their packhorses looked gigantic. A ranchero in broad-brimmed leather sombrero and gay serape took a husk cigarillo from his mouth far enough to give them a grudging *"Buenos días."*

Curdy waved toward a huddle of adobe buildings on the bank of a swift-rushing stream, a huge waterwheel turning in the current. "Sim Turley's mill and distillery on Arroyo Hondo. Sim's American but he makes the best Taos Lightnin' in Mexico. *Aguardiente,* they calls it here, but Taos Lightnin's more fittin'. When a bolt or two of that hits a feller, he don't give a hang about nothin'."

Then they were approaching San Fernandez, a jumble of adobe buildings surrounding a central plaza and enclosed by an outer wall for defense against the frequent Indian raids. Everything gave off a dazzling glitter from a coating of whitewash mixed with mica flakes. In front of each house was a dome-shaped mud oven for baking *biscoches,* a light, sweet, white biscuit that was a favorite of hungry mountain men.

Groups of dark-eyed beauties, many balancing water jars on their heads, gave them flashing smiles as dazzling as the micaflecked walls. The men, squatting in the shade, glared at them in sullen silence as they passed.

Curdy chuckled. "The gals are pure froze on Americans, but their men ain't of the same mind *a*-tall. Ever' one's got a knife a foot long under his serape, jest itchin' to tickle our ribs. Only reason they don't is account of all the money we spends. Without us, a dollar or two in a month is the most they'd see in their whole lives."

As they rode into the plaza a knot of buckskin-clad figures converged on them with shouts of greeting. "Matt, you old hoss! An' Dick hisself! Light down an' ease the kinks. You musta come over Sangree Pass. We just come in over Raton Pass and didn't see no fresh trail."

The next moment they were pumping hands and pounding

backs with Kit Carson, big Rube Herring, Marcellin St. Vrain, Baptiste Charbonneau and half a dozen other mountain men, on their way to the mountains.

"Dick," Marcellin said, black eyes dancing, "you told me you'd never seen a fandango. Well, hoss, you're going to see one tonight. We've got a ring-tailed roarer fixed up at the sala of Miguel Vicente, starting at sundown. We'll pick you up at the store."

They broke away at last and led their packhorses to the Bent & St. Vrain establishment. Since they were bringing their string anyhow to carry back Dick's peltry, they had brought a few loads of company merchandise on the down trip. Ceran St. Vrain greeted them warmly and sent Mexican helpers to unload. "Your plews are in top condition, Dick. I had the boys open the packs just last week and shake them all out to make sure no moths were eating them. Whenever you're ready to leave, they'll load up for you."

"I'm obliged," Dick said. "The way winter's setting in back there, I figure we'd better get started back tomorrow if we aim to get through before spring."

He prowled the shadowy cavern of the store, piled to the beamed ceiling with a variety of merchandise, feeling a stirring excitement. In a way it must be nice to spread your goods in one place and let the customers come to you. Maybe some day in the future, when he was tired of danger and adventure, he might try a hand at storekeeping himself.

That day he had his first taste of red-hot Mexican chile, scooped up with rolled tortillas like unsweetened flapjacks, and until the fire in his mouth cooled he had all the excitement he could handle.

Promptly at sundown the boisterous crowd descended to drag him to the fandango. "Leave your rifle," Kit Carson told him, "but keep those two pups loaded and primed in your belt and wear your knife. This promises to be a first-rate fandango and you'll need them for sure before the night's over."

The house of Miguel Vicente was north of the plaza, behind the house of Ceran St. Vrain. A crowd was already gathered and the stirring beat of a Mexican guitar and an Indian *tombé* drum throbbed on the soft night air. Dick ducked through a low doorway and into a big, whitewashed room, low-ceilinged and dimly lighted.

All the women of the town, young and old, seemed to have crowded into one end of the room, making a vivid splash of color in their gay Mexican costumes decked with jewelry. All were laughing and chattering, their black eyes flashing with excitement. Ever since he came West Dick had heard the mountain men rave over the Taos beauties. Staring at them now, he decided not a word of those rhapsodies had been exaggerated.

A few Mexican men were dancing, swinging their partners in graceful circles. The majority, however, leaned against the walls wrapped in their serapes, puffing their endless cigarillos and glowering sullenly at the scene of gaiety.

Inside the doorway, Dick's companions deserted him abruptly to storm across the room with whoops and wolf howls. There was no ceremony of greeting, no polite bowing and asking for a dance. Each trapper seized a girl around the waist and swung her out onto the floor with all the finesse of a hunter wrestling a grizzly. Dick expected squeals of protest but all he heard were shrieks of delight.

He found a place by the wall and stared in open astonishment. Matt Curdy's description of the dancing had been more accurate than Dick realized. Big Rube Herring was whirling his slender partner through his own athletic version of an Indian buffalo dance. The rest were spinning, stomping, kicking, and leaping in a bedlam of howls and shrieks of laughter. The few Mexicans who had been dancing were powerless to buck the raging maelstrom. After some rude and violent collisions, most of them gave up and joined the sullen watchers on the sidelines.

From his shadowy corner, Dick could see why the Mexican

word fandango could be translated as either a dance or a fight. He wondered how the girls could stand the pace until he saw that after a few whirls each trapper abandoned his partner and seized another from the waiting group.

Dick had no intention whatever of taking part in the ridiculous spectacle. Nevertheless the insistent, throbbing beat of the music began to get hold of him, and he found his fingers tapping and his feet shuffling to the rhythm. The antics of the dancers began to look a little less ridiculous.

He was so intent on the dancers that the girl spoke to him twice before he realized she was there. He looked down and gulped. She was tiny and slender, looking up at him with bright, laughing eyes that were both admiring and inviting. She said something in tinkling Spanish and tugged his arms.

Dick could feel himself blushing. "Uh . . . thanks, Miss . . . Senorita . . . but I don't dance. I'm just watching my friends . . ."

There was surprising strength in the slender hands that caught hold of his wrists. He was still mumbling excuses when he found himself out on the floor, his hands firmly pinned to a slim waist. Laughing merrily at his embarrassment, the girl began a gliding circle and Dick had to turn with her.

A powerful hand slammed him on the back and Matt Curdy's voice bawled, "Don't jest stand there, hoss. *Stomp* it!"

Dick was never quite clear how it happened but suddenly he found himself bobbing and bouncing and twirling to the compelling tempo of the music. Kit Carson whirled by, yelling, "You're a gone coon now, Dick boy!" and Dick whooped back in sheer high spirits.

He wanted to find out the name of his vivacious partner and to try out some of the halting Spanish he had picked up at Bent's Fort. He made a couple of earnest tries but his voice was lost in the din and the exertions of the dance left little breath for conversation.

He never did find out exactly how or where the fight started.

He knew only that he was beginning to get the hang of the dancing when the music stopped with a discordant clash. There came a yell of anger, shrieks of fright. His partner twisted away and was lost in the surging crowd.

Rube Herring's bellow rose. Dick caught a startling glimpse of a Mexican figure flying through the air to crash against the wall. Then it seemed that fighting was going on all over the floor. He saw the slender figure of Kit Carson jerking and reeling, trying to break the grip of Mexicans who were hanging onto both his arms. A third man, poising a long, slender knife, was circling with them, trying to get a clear jab at Kit's unprotected back.

Dick loosed a roar of wordless fury and leaped. His big fist caught the knife wielder behind the ear with sledgehammer force. The Mexican slammed forward into a surging mass of his compatriots and collapsed in a limp sprawl. At the same moment, Kit planted his feet and brought his extended arms around in a snapping jerk. The two figures clinging to his wrists were swept into one, their heads slamming together with an audible crash.

"Thanks, Dick," Kit yelled above the din. "Close up so we can cover each other's backs."

Dick found himself with the rest of the Americans, bunched in front of the corner where the musicians had sat. The women had vanished, scuttling out into the night at the first outbreak of trouble. Now, between the trappers and the only door was a solid wall of angry Mexican men with knives in their hands and murder in their eyes.

Matt Curdy had his Green River blade out. "Draw your pups, Dick. Again' that mob we'll likely go under, but we'll take a few *pelados* with us.

"Hold it!" Kit said sharply. "If blood gets spilled we'll all end up in the *calabozo,* if we don't dance our next fandango on the end of a rope."

He looked around and spied the heavy three-legged stool on

which the guitar player had perched. In a bound he caught it up and slammed it against the wall, wrenching off the heavy legs. He tossed one to big Rube Herring and one to Dick. Swinging the third in whistling arcs, he shouted, "Let's go, hosses! We'll open a path to the door while you cover our backs."

With a bloodcurdling war whoop he sprang at the massed Mexicans, the others howling at his heels. The club made a hollow ringing thump on an unprotected skull.

Dick saw a fiercely moustached Mexican flip his knife into the air, catch it by the blade and poise it to throw. He swung his club at the lifted wrist and heard the snap of breaking bones, a yell of pain as the knife flew across the room. Then he was clubbing furiously right and left and the foe was giving way before their relentless drive.

The next moment a broad path to the door was cleared and they were crowding through into the night, leaving at least a dozen unconscious figures sprawled on the floor. They burst out into the moonlit plaza and Kit threw out his arms to halt their dash.

"We can ease off now. They've had a bellyful of us for one night. Anyhow, it ain't their style to push a fight out in the open where we aren't cornered and outnumbered. How did we come out of it this time? Anybody hurt?"

Marcellin had a lump on his head and a bloody nose. Charbonneau had a shallow knife gash on one arm, and a couple of the others had been lightly pinked.

"Not bad," Curdy said. "I've seed a crowd banged up wuss than this, just breakin' mules." He turned to Dick. "Well, hoss, have you made up your mind yet whether a fandango is a dance or a fight?"

Dick drew a deep breath and laughed, feeling suddenly loose and easy and full of high, happy spirits. "You were right about it's being both, Matt. And you know, whichever part of it I get to thinking back on, it was about the most exciting night I've had in my whole life."

14

THEY left the soft, springlike warmth of the Taos valley and rode over the Pass into the fury of winter. An icy wind cut at their faces and burned in their nostrils, piling the season's first snow into drifts that stood breast-high to the horses. After a few hours of floundering struggle, Dick and Curdy dismounted and walked ahead to break a path for the exhausted animals.

It was into the afternoon when Dick, peering through the shifting curtain of blowing snow, spied a dark object threshing in a snowdrift. He threw up his gun but before his sights settled he glimpsed what appeared to be a waving arm.

"It's a man, Matt," he yelled above the wind. "Come on."

They wallowed their way to the figure and stopped, staring. It was not a man but a woman, an Indian girl, barefoot and shivering in a few shreds of tattered blanket. The girl looked up at them in numb misery and whimpered a few words Dick recognized as Arapaho. He whirled to his horse, tearing at the lashings that held his sleeping robes behind his saddle.

"Help me get her wrapped up and onto a horse, Matt. Then look for some place with shelter and wood so we can build up a big fire."

An hour later they found a spot in a clump of cottonwoods. With a hot fire roaring and plenty of rich stew to restore her strength, the girl told her story by signs and speech. Her village had been surprised by an overpowering war party of Utes and many Arapaho warriors killed. She and a number of other women were taken prisoner.

On the way to the Ute village, she had managed to escape and find her way back over the mountains until caught in the winter storm. Without weapon or fire and only the scrap of clothing, she had been too starved and frozen to go further when Dick and Matt discovered her.

The next morning dawned clear and cold. By rearranging their load of plews, Dick freed one of the packhorses for her to ride. They rigged a saddle from a spare apishamore—a soft elkskin saddle blanket—and wrapped her in their warmest buffalo robes before taking the trail.

By the second day she had recovered most of her strength. The third morning she told them by excited signs that her village was only a short distance north of their trail.

"You can't blame her for wanting to get back to her home and friends," Dick said. By signs and his small stock of Arapaho words, he told her, "If it is your wish, take the robes and the horse and what food you need and go on to your village. You may keep horse and robes until your people come to Bent's Fort again or until I visit your village when the snow is gone."

The Indian girl seized his hand, pressed it hard for a moment, looking deep into his eyes, and rode off without a word. They watched horse and rider disappear over a snowy ridge and then turned back to their arduous trailbreaking.

They were breaking camp the next morning when Curdy looked up and said softly, "Dick, either we got visitors or the goshdangdest Injun fight of our lives comin' up."

Dick whirled and saw a seemingly endless column of Indian riders streaming over the hills. He stared around, but if there was any shelter within reach, the snow concealed it. The only alternative would be to shoot their horses and use the carcasses for a shielding wall. More than one party of hunters or trappers had survived attack by overwhelming numbers through such a desperate stratagem.

While he hesitated, the first rays of the rising sun caught the Indian column in their brightness and his breath rushed out.

"It's all right, Matt. They're Arapahoes and they aren't carrying shields or painted for war."

The newcomers proved to be virtually the whole surviving village of the girl they had saved, hastening to return the loaned property and show their deep gratitude. As gifts they brought beautifully tanned robes and two of the finest Indian ponies the Americans had ever seen.

Never before had either Dick or Matt seen Indians express their emotions so openly and warmly. When they finally broke away to continue their journey, Curdy said thoughtfully, "You know, Dick, if we'd been of a mind to, I bet we could have got ourselves made high chiefs of the whole blame 'Rapaho Nation today."

For the rest of their lives every time either man went anywhere near an Arapaho village he was literally kidnaped for royal entertainment. Even small children heard the story from elders and followed Dick around with bright-eyed adoration. Within a short time the act of simple kindness was to prove for Dick one of the most rewarding gestures he had ever made.

That winter the price of beaver plews had fallen so low that Dick renounced trapping as his royal road to riches. Except for an occasional brief, nostalgic trip into the mountains, he never again took up the arduous occupation. Instead, he signed on as meat hunter for Bent's Fort, a job arduous enough in itself, with the huge and varying population of the fort consuming an average of ten pounds of meat per day per person. While the mainstay was buffalo, the diet had to be varied frequently with bear, deer, elk, and antelope.

Such hunting was a highly organized activity. Dick worked with two skilled butchers and a pack or wagon train to haul in the meat. Many times his kills ran as high as thirty buffalo a day.

He rode a common horse and led his highly trained buffalo runner to use only when needed. Wherever possible he preferred to get downwind of a herd and work up close enough to pick off his choice from a stand. As long as the buffalo could not sight or smell him, they milled about in confusion without stampeding, and dropping the day's supply in one spot made the work of his butchers easier. When that proved impossible— and often just for the excitement of the chase—he switched to his buffalo horse and rode down his selected quarry, trying to drop each with a close-range shot through the neck. While he enjoyed the chase he was never fond of the slaughter and was constantly on the lookout for some new and interesting opportunity for profit.

In his two beaver expeditions he had made a considerable amount of money and he spent it with a prodigal hand. Old mountain men who wanted to finance a grand fandango at Taos or simply to quench a long-building thirst with comrades found Dick a soft touch. With Taos Lightning selling at $25 a jug, it took a lot of money to balance off the dry months in the mountains.

As an investment, he financed an elaborate trading expedition for some friends. On the way out the train was attacked by hostile Indians, the men killed, the wagons looted and burned. Dick sustained a total loss of several thousand dollars. One day he awoke to the bitter realization that he was practically broke. Sadly he wrote his parents that his return to Christian County, Kentucky, would have to be postponed another year or two until he had recouped his losses.

On one of his hunts Dick discovered a pair of orphaned buffalo calves. Moved by a combination of pity and curiosity, he had them loaded on the wagon and taken to the fort where he persuaded a cow that had lost her calf to adopt the ungainly pair. They thrived so well that he began to consider the possibility of raising buffalo instead of having to run meat all over the prairie.

On the site of present-day Pueblo, Colorado, he had a number of heavy corrals built and here he established the first commercial buffalo farm in the world. With forty-four buffalo calves collected by hunters and forty milch cows as foster mothers, he was on the way to becoming the Buffalo King.

Dick had planned to make his ranch a source of meat supply for the fort but matters turned out differently. When his herd was three years old a man who bought animals for zoos in the East and in Europe got wind of it and bought Dick's entire supply. A number wound up in New York's Central Park Zoo and many were shipped abroad.

With a handful of herders, Dick drove his buffalo across the Plains for delivery to the buyer at Kansas City. Their supplies were carried in wagons drawn by buffalo teams he had broken to yoke and harness like oxen, to the amazement of Indians and Plainsmen. Decades later, when conservationists were fighting to save the buffalo from extinction, they turned back to Dick's success for tips on domesticating the great beasts.

Meanwhile, through the bitter winter of 1840 he had other irons in the fire, some of them productive of perilous adventures. Bent & St. Vrain appointed him a special courier to carry messages and large supplies of cash between the fort, the store in Taos, and the new Fort Lookout, renamed Fort St. Vrain, up on the South Platte.

Early that winter his first courier trip brought him about as close to losing his scalp as he ever cared to come. Along the way he planned to spend a night in the lodge of Arapaho Chief Buffalo Billy, in whose village Dick was so extravagantly idolized and lavishly entertained. This chief, with two other Arapaho chiefs, Roman Nose and Big Mouth, had combined to winter their people in a village of some six hundred lodges at the mouth of Crow Creek.

Traveling was not too bad at first but presently Dick ran into a broad belt where high winds had piled the heavy snow into drifts six and eight feet deep. By the time they reached the open country beyond, his horse was too exhausted to carry him another step. The Arapaho village was still thirty miles ahead but Dick had no choice. He let the shivering animal go free, buried his saddle and bridle under the deepest drift, and set off on foot to finish his journey, knowing he could have his pick of fresh ponies at the village.

The hike itself was no staggering project in his mind. The country from here on was flat and open and the high winds kept it swept almost clean of snow. It was bitterly cold but jogging at a steady pace would keep his blood moving.

His one big worry was the possibility of encountering hostile Indians. Alone and on foot, he would be easy prey for a mounted war party and little better off against a band on foot. So he traveled with his head swiveling endlessly, his eyes aching from searching the white glare.

As the day wore on without a sign of enemies he began to feel there really might be something in the Wootton luck the scouts spoke of with mild awe. By midafternoon the sight of familiar landmarks told him the Arapaho village was little more than six miles ahead and he relaxed a little.

Suddenly he caught the faintest flicker of movement from the corner of his eye. Some four or five hundred yards to his right a low ridge paralleled his path. A line of black shapes was coming over the crest and down the slope toward him. For a moment he had the wild, wishful thought that it was a herd of antelope. He squinted into the snow glare and made out the forms of at least twenty Indians on foot. Then his heart lurched as he recognized the high, bristling, roached scalp lock of Pawnee warriors. Already winded and weary from his long trot, he faced the simple alternative of dying there in the snow or making a desperate run for it. He put his head down and the snow spurted from his moccasins. With yells of rage the Pawnees took after him.

He ran as he had never in his life run before. Risking a quick glance over his shoulder, he saw that two fleeter warriors had forged well ahead of the rest and were slowly but surely gaining on him. His lungs ached and his throat flamed with every sobbing breath and the pound of blood was a thunder in his ears, but somehow he found an extra surge of speed.

Close to three miles had lurched by before Dick dared look

again. One Pawnee was within two hundred yards, close enough for the mask of strain and rage on his face to be plainly visible. The second warrior was perhaps a hundred yards behind the first, with the others closely bunched behind. Dick was sorely tempted to whirl and try a shot at the leading Pawnee, but he was so wracked by the effort of breathing that he was afraid of missing, with no time to reload. He ran on.

He was beginning to stumble a little. The ragged pound of his moccasins beat out the endless refrain: *Three more miles . . . Three more miles*. He tried to see ahead, to search out the haven of the Arapaho village but the landscape blurred in his misted vision.

He stumbled and almost tripped before he realized he had breasted a low rise and was running down a sloping hillside littered with snowcapped rocks. Flicking a quick look back, he saw that for a brief moment he was hidden by the hill's crest from even his closest pursuer.

The Wootton luck still held. He swerved and threw himself behind a rock, using the top for a rest to steady his Hawken rifle. The Pawnee burst up over the hill and full into his sights. He squeezed the trigger and saw the savage fling up his arms, his tomahawk pinwheeling off into the snow. The pumping legs folded and tangled and he came rolling over and over down the slope, leaving a trail of crimson blots on the dazzling white.

Dick whirled and fled again, reloading as he ran, his cold-numbed hands making clumsy work of it. When he looked again, the second pursuer had dropped back to the main pack, beyond rifle range but still coming doggedly on. Dick was stumbling now with almost every step, his knees rubbery, his lungs bursting.

The distant forest of pale dun cones swam in his vision a full minute before his numb brain gave them meaning and identity.

The Arapaho village!

Behind him the Pawnees discovered the village at the same

moment and skidded to a jolting halt. There was brief milling confusion and uncertainty. Then they were running again, this time streaming back up the trail in a desperate race to put a low hill between themselves and enemy eyes.

They were already too late. In the village, sharp eyes had seen and recognized the staggering figure of Cut-Hand and then the identity of his pursuers. Minutes later forty mounted warriors were pounding toward Dick, their war whoops ringing on the frosty air. They swirled around him, dropping the reins of a saddled pony for him, then raced on after the enemy.

Dick was in a wild fury to ride with them and settle his personal score but when he tried to mount, his exhausted muscles refused to lift him into the saddle. In the end he had to be content with clinging to a stirrup and letting the pony half-drag him to the village. An hour or so later the warriors galloped in, yipping in triumph and waving seventeen fresh Pawnee scalps.

That night Dick was guest of honor at the most tumultuous and colorful scalp dance and victory celebration he had ever witnessed. The Arapahoes eclipsed all their previous displays of friendship and gratitude. Not only had he delivered a host of their fiercest enemy into their hands but had given them an opportunity to further repay an obligation deeply felt.

So warm was the feeling between them that Dick took to spending most of his free time that winter at the village. He hunted with them, raced ponies against them, learned their games, and came to know them more intimately than perhaps any other white man in the West. The Arapaho warriors were particularly awed by Dick's marksmanship with the rifle. On the hunts they invariably deferred to him whenever a particularly difficult or important shot was to be made.

In the early spring Dick decided to turn their close association to profit and made up a packtrain of goods for Arapaho trade. He had no more than reached the village when a late-season blizzard, by far the worst of the winter, howled down from the north to engulf the land.

Day after day they huddled around the fires, trapped by the curtain of whipping snow so thick it concealed even adjoining lodges from one another. The food supply dwindled and vanished, and still there was no break in the fury of the storm. In desperation they were finally reduced to boiling moccasins, scraps of robes, and even their precious pipe cases for the little nourishment the old leather could yield. "I got about as hungry as a man ever gets," Dick remembered afterward.

At the first sign of a break in the storm he took his gun and plunged out in search of anything edible. Throughout the blizzard the weather had remained unseasonably warm and the deep, heavy snow made every step an effort. He finally reached the bank of the South Platte, exhausted and bitter, not having seen a sign of animal life anywhere in the white and silent land.

The river was running in flood and choked with jagged masses of breaking ice. As he stood panting, staring across the wild scene, his eye caught a flicker of movement on the opposite shore. Squinting, he made out the form of a wild goose crouched in the snow.

Suddenly a hundred and fifty yards of ice-choked river became a rivulet in his hungry eyes. The gun leaped up and sent its crashing echoes over the snow. The goose lurched up, flopped crazily, and was still with wings widespread. Dick took a deep breath, propped his rifle against a tree, and plunged in. He came back with the neck of the dead goose clutched in his teeth, using both hands to claw his way through the floes.

Stumbling back to the village with his precious lifesaving burden, icy water squashing in his moccasins and his buckskins beginning to freeze on his body, he thought, "Let Matt talk all he wants about fat cow and fleece fat and painter. There ain't a meat on earth that can taste as good as this tough old goose is going to when it's boiled out."

15

Dick's courier trips proved so useful and dependable that Bent & St. Vrain were encouraged to inaugurate a regular weekly express run between their farflung posts. He made many of the runs, at first, traveling alone or with one or two helpers and a packtrain. At times the packs carried as much as sixty thousand dollars in silver through the wildest country, but never once was he attacked or even seriously threatened.

Other men could have used a touch of the Wootton luck in those violent days. Down on Timpas Creek the Pawnees struck a packtrain led by twenty-year-old Marcellin St. Vrain with disastrous results. One of his men was killed and three wounded. The Indians made off with three horses and nine pack mules loaded with more than three thousand dollars' worth of Bent & St. Vrain goods. Soon after this a band of Comanches swirled past Bent's Fort, killed the horse guard almost in the shadow of the wall, and ran off the entire herd.

In the fall of 1841 Dick came in from one of his trips to find a fresh grave just outside the main gate. The old French tailor was setting out a thick bed of cactus on top to keep the wolves from digging up the body. With a stab of dark foreboding, Dick reined in. "Who's dead?"

The Frenchman's lip trembled. "Monsieur Robert."

Inside, Dick got the tragic story. The handsome Robert, youngest of the Bent brothers, had been coming up the Arkansas with a train when he spied a buffalo. He dashed recklessly out after it and into the hands of Comanches stalking the same meat.

His companions saw him struck down and scalped before they could ride to his rescue.

The tragedy struck Dick deeply. Robert and Dick had been almost of the same age and had come West at nearly the same time. The loss was a sharp reminder of the perils Dick himself faced daily, but it did nothing to curb his own reckless spirit. Shortly afterward he gave up regular express runs as offering neither the adventure nor the riches he craved. He found instead a new enterprise that promised a full measure of both.

At that time the Utes had signed a brief, uneasy peace with the white man and were eager to trade for his goods. However, despite the promise of fabulous profit, no traders were anxious to jump into that field. One reason was the well-known fickleness of Ute friendship. The other was that to reach them the traders had to cross Apache country, and the Apaches were waging a fierce and relentless war against all white men.

For Dick, the combination of peril and profit was irresistible. In the winter of 1843 he posted a two thousand dollar bond for a government license to trade with the Utes and assembled a packtrain of goods he knew would tickle their fancy. His stock consisted of vermilion, ochre, and other war paints, beads, knives, ammunition, and fifty trade muskets.

Then, to the horror of Matt Curdy and others at the fort, he decided against taking a strong party of guards and helpers. "I know all that country too well to need a guide and scouts. I'm only taking Tanglefoot along as my helper and second gun."

Tanglefoot was a Delaware Indian, noted for both his courage and his marksmanship. He had traveled frequently with both Charles and William and had distinguished himself in numerous encounters with hostile bands.

On the morning of their departure, Curdy shook hands soberly. "Once you get an idee in that thick skull of yourn, Dick, you're mule-stubborn on changing it. I jest hope this ain't your last one. If I don't see you back here comes spring, I'll figure the Wootton luck has finally petered out."

Dick's destination was a large village of Utes known to be moving around in the Canadian River country of the Texas Panhandle. The journey was uneventful as the two moved south and crossed Raton Pass. On Sugarite Creek they encountered a Mexican hunter who told them the Ute village was only a few miles downstream. Eight miles further on they came to a village of some forty lodges. A few hundred yards back stood a small clump of cottonwoods, offering shade, shelter, and ample firewood.

"There's a ready-made camping spot," Dick decided. He looked at the sun slanting toward the mountaintops. "It'll be getting dark shortly. We'd better set up camp while we've still got daylight and then hunt up the Ute chief and talk trade."

Curiously, except for the inevitable snarling dogs, the village seemed strangely deserted. Two or three old men and a few squaws gaped at them furtively but no one approached. Dick was puzzled. "I wonder what's wrong. It isn't natural not to have some braves rushing out to see who we are."

Tanglefoot shrugged. "Who know what in mind of Ute . . . except always hope to cut throat and lift hair."

Presently, taking picket rope and pin, the Delaware led their riding horses toward a patch of rich grass nearer the lodges. He was nearly there when Dick saw him stop abruptly, then whirl and come back almost at a run. Under the bronze, his face looked pale.

"What's the trouble?" Dick demanded as he stumbled in.

"Plenty heap trouble. This not Ute village. Tanglefoot get close look at marking. This Apache village."

Dick's breath locked. He had a feeling that ice was congealing in his veins. He hissed, "Start packing up as fast as you can. All the warriors must be out on a hunt. Our only hope is to put on all the miles we can before they come back and find we've been here."

Pushing the packhorses to their limit, they covered several miles before darkness closed in. They were on the edge of a grove of cottonwoods that had been ravaged by some past storm. Along the edge the trunks of fallen trees offered defensible barricades. They dismounted and tied the horses close among the trees.

"Start unpacking those fifty guns," Dick said. "We'll load them all and lay them out so all we have to do is grab and shoot. If they try to charge, they'll think they've run into an army."

There was no sleep for either that night. Shortly after daylight a band of Apaches appeared, following their trail. At the sight of the log barricade literally bristling with guns, the Indians stopped for a long conference. At last three painted Apaches rode forward, making peace signs. They halted some distance back when Dick stepped into sight, his own rifle ready.

"We come in peace," the leader signed. "We are told that the white brother has goods to trade. If we can come into your camp and examine the goods, we will do much business."

"And I know what kind of business those devils have in mind," Dick muttered grimly. "Nothing doing." His hands moved, making the gestures of flat refusal. He ended with a wave at the row of muskets lined along a great log, all pointing toward the Apaches. "We have only a great many guns and much ammunition, and these, as you can see, are for our use, not for trade."

The three turned away, glaring fiercely, and rejoined their companions. For what seemed an eternity to Dick they sat their restive ponies, studying the camp and talking. Suddenly, with yells of rage, they whirled and raced off up the creek.

"Come on," Dick barked. "They've probably gone for the rest of their bunch and we'd better not be around when they come back. Forty lodges means a hundred warriors at least, and Apaches don't bluff worth a dang."

They rode all day at a furious pace, watching their back trail and frequently riding in the creek to obliterate their tracks. By nightfall it was obvious that they were not being pursued, probably because the Apaches had no wish to run into a strong party of Utes who would probably side with their white ally.

Next day they found the big Ute village and almost at once began to wish they hadn't. Tanglefoot, who spoke some Ute, rode forward and returned shortly in near-panic. "Ute big chief heap sick, soon die. All Utes not trade, not hunt, just mourn and wait. We better go heap fast."

"After coming all this way? Not by a jugful. If we can't coax them into trading now, we'll just wait until the old boy goes under and then do our business."

"Cut-Hand not understand Ute custom. When chief die, people kill first strangers they meet so chief's spirit have company on trail to happy hunting ground."

Dick felt a chill touch his spine. Then his jaw set and he swung a pack of trade goods to his shoulder. "You wait here, ready to move if I come back running. I'll go see what the sittuation is and what our chances are of keeping our hair."

The lodge of Chief High Horn was hot and close and rank with the stench of sickness. One look at the old man's wasted body and fever-bright eyes told Dick the chief was beyond hope, although he might linger for days. He had no idea what the malady might be but it was clearly fatal. When the Utes crowded around, begging him to use white man's medicine, he shook his head firmly. In the first place, he knew no medicine could help now, and in the second, when the old man did die, it would be too easy to blame any medicine of his.

"I have no white man's medicine," he signed, "but I do have fine goods to trade."

He opened his pack and spread the beads and paints and fine knives on a blanket. The Indians stared with black, inscrutable eyes and gave no response to his signs. But when he exhibited the trade musket he carried, he was certain he saw a spark of veiled interest in many eyes.

On the way back to his packtrain, Dick saw piles of beautifully tanned robes. In the grazing herd outside the village were a great number of splendid mules and ponies that would bring top prices at Bent's Fort. The sight helped him arrive at a difficult and dangerous decision.

"Start unpacking," he told Tanglefoot. "I figure the old man will hang on four or five days yet. That'll still give us time to stir up their trading blood if I stay with them and keep working at it. I've arranged for us to move into a lodge right next to the chief's so we can check on his condition every day and clear out if he gets much worse."

The Delaware gave him a horrified look but he led their packhorses to the indicated lodge. That night they encountered another unpleasant phase of Dick's gamble. Ute custom forbade hunting during a chief's illness so the village was subsisting entirely on its dog pack. Only the toughest and scrawniest remained but rather than waste time hunting, Dick forced himself to share the gamy mess.

For two days Dick spread his goods, coaxing, wheedling, using every wile to tempt the Indians into breaking their wall of reticence. Day by day the tension grew as the old chief steadily weakened. Even Tanglefoot's nerves frayed and he begged passionately for Dick to give up and flee while there was still time.

"Not yet," Dick said stubbornly. "He's weakening, but so are they, and I've got a feeling they'll break first. If we run out now, we'll have to pack everything back through Apache country and write the whole winter off as a dead loss."

On the afternoon of the third day he tried a desperate ploy. Trade muskets were excellent for killing buffalo at close range but fantastically inaccurate at a distance. That day, with the Indians watching in sullen silence, he set up a stick for a target, paced off a hundred and fifty yards, and selected the best of his stock of fusils. He loaded with extreme care, patching the ball to insure maximum accuracy. He steadied the sights, held his breath, and fired. The target stick flew into splinters.

The next moment Indians were swarming around, chattering

excitedly and passing the gun from hand to hand. When Dick ran for the lodge where his stock was waiting, they trailed after him, their former reticence forgotten in the face of this miracle of marksmanship.

Never had Dick seen trading go so fast or with so little haggling. At sundown they built up a blazing fire and went on into the night. By the following noon every item was gone and Dick and Tanglefoot were riding out of camp with a fabulous stock of peltries and a long string of horses and mules.

"We made it, Tanglefoot," Dick cried exultantly.

"Not yet," the Delaware grunted, twisting around to stare back at the village. "Tanglefoot look at chief. Bad. Bad. Him blow bubbles mouth. Better we go heap far heap fast."

They learned later that the chief lived for two days after their departure, but they never found out what hapless stranger was dispatched to accompany him on his spirit journey.

16

On the way back Dick stopped to visit at Pueblo, the new adobe fort and trading post on the upper Arkansas at the mouth of Fountain Creek. This had been put up the previous summer by a combine of traders and trappers, including Alex Barclay, formerly a factor at Bent's Fort, and the famous mountain man, mulatto Jim Beckwourth.

By comparison with Bent's Fort Pueblo was small and shoddy, but it had the advantage of being much closer to Taos and the mountains. Dick found a number of acquaintances there, including Beckwourth and the gaunt, tough, eccentric old Bill Williams. They gave him a boisterous greeting and settled down to exchange the news of the winter's activities.

"Friend o' yourn was jest here askin' about you, Dick," old Bill said in his high, querulous whine. "Seemed right anxious to meet up with you. Too bad he rid off yistiddy."

"Who was that?" Dick asked.

Old Bill gave him a sly, twisted grin. "Feller by the name o' Noah Carse."

Dick stiffened, his face going blank and cold. "I reckon Carse knows where to find me if he's that set on it."

"It strikes this chile," Beckwourth said in his soft drawl, "thet meetin' up with yuh face to face in a crowd wa'n't quite whut that varmint had in mind. Was I you, hoss, I'd keep both eyes peeled constant. Back-shootin' from the bushes is more the style he's froze to."

"Thanks," Dick said grimly. "I'll keep a sharp lookout."

Will Tharp, a noted trader, spoke up. "Where you aimin' to sell your Ute takin's, Dick?"

"Why, at Bent's Fort, I guess. Unless you or Alex are offering better prices."

"I can get you three times their price or better back East," Tharp said. "I'm taking a train straight through to Kansas City, leaving day after tomorrow. They're so plumb hungry to beat out Westport and Independence for trade that they're offering by far the highest prices on the river. I can get you up to a hundred dollars for a mule that'd fetch maybe twenty-thirty dollars from Bent's. Why not let me take your stock along and sell it for you where the fat money is?"

Dick's eyes glistened with interest. The mules had cost him around eight dollars each in trade goods and the prospect of turning so splendid a profit was an irresistible lure. On the other hand, he felt an obligation to do what business he could with Bent & St. Vrain. In the end he compromised. Thirteen mules loaded with fine peltry were left behind with Tharp while he took the remainder in to Bent's Fort.

His dream of wealth was rudely shattered some two months later when a returning wagon train brought grim news. "Comanches struck Tharp's train in Kansas. Tharp and every one of his men were killed, their stock taken, and the wagons plundered and burned."

Dick sadly wrote off his losses and went back to earning his fortune the slower, harder way. He took up his old job of meat hunter for the fort at a dollar a day but that seemed lean pickings compared to the Indian trade. He soon got together a stock of trade goods and took a train up to old Yellow Wolf's village of Cheyennes in the Colorado mountains.

Yellow Wolf, nearing sixty, was small for a Cheyenne but wiry and tough as rawhide. He was principal chief of the Hevha-Itanio, the Hairy-Rope Clan, famed as the first Indians to braid lariats from buffalo neck hair instead of rawhide strips. Yellow Wolf was famous for his skill in capturing wild mustangs as well as in stealing enemy horses, and consequently his village boasted the finest herds on the Plains. A staunch friend of the whites, he had helped William Bent select the location for Bent's Fort and had been the first to bring his people in to trade.

Consequently, Dick's expedition was as profitable as it was uneventful. While at the village he became especially friendly with the chief's young cousin, Little Wolf, already the champion long distance runner of the Cheyennes and destined to become one of the greatest of all their leaders.

In the early winter Dick resumed his trade with the Utes and found it richly rewarding. They were so hungry for goods that it was not unusual for him to do two thousand dollars' worth of business within half a day. They had learned to respect and trust him so implicitly that they began asking him to meet them at a prearranged rendezvous after so many moons. They kept these appointments religiously, bringing the finest horses and mules and flatly refusing to do business with any other trader.

He had never been so prosperous—or so bored. In all his trips he saw not one sign of hostile Indians, nor did he encounter any other perils to bring spice to the job.

In the fall he and Matt Curdy rode up to the new Fort St. Vrain on the South Platte. This was a smaller copy of Bent's Fort, its walls running sixty by a hundred and thirty feet including walled corral. Marcellin was in charge and a number of mountain men, including Kit Carson, made it their base of operations. Marcellin was also playing reluctant host to some blue-blood sports from St. Louis, out for some hunting and frontier adventure.

By the end of his first day, Dick agreed with the mountain men that the sports were about the loudest mouthed pack of windbags west of the Mississippi. Practically every time the five went out to hunt, they returned with some outrageous tale of an encounter with hostile Indians. "Yes sir, there we were, creeping up on the buffalo herd when we saw this war party of forty or fifty Pawnees creeping up on us. You fellers are supposed to be the big Indian fighters. What would you have done?"

Old Bat Clutie spat into the fire and said dryly, "I reckon I'd have done the same thing you did—skeedaddle so fast my leggin's 'd smoke."

One of the sportsmen, a windy character named Alexander, snorted contemptuously. "You probably would have, but not us. We ups with our rifles and let fly, and every shot went dead center. When the Pawnees saw our five rifles and five dead Indians on the ground, they hightailed it out of there in a hurry."

"Only five Injuns with five shots?" Dick asked innocently. "Us fellers usually likes to wait until they're lined up so we can drill three or four redskins with the one rifle ball."

A few days later the five announced their intention to go after wild cherries they had seen ripening in a dense thicket down the river. "There was plenty of Indian sign around so I imagine we'll get a few redskins along with the fruit."

Dick looked across and met Matt's eyes. The two got up at once and walked outside. "Dick, if you're thinkin' the same thing I'm thinkin', you've got the kind of nasty, sneaky mind I'd admire to go along with."

Presently the five reached the thicket, left their horses and guns, and scattered to pick cherries, each with his own basket. Without warning, pistols banged and a chorus of Comanche war whoops split the air. The fearless Indian fighters dropped their baskets, jumped on their horses, and fled in such panic that they left their guns behind. They burst into the fort to pant out a story of bloody battle.

"There were hundreds of Indians, attacking from all sides. We kept killing them until our ammunition ran out and then we made a charge and broke out. We lost our guns swimming the Platte to shake them off our trail."

At this point, Dick and Matt rode in, smiling with bland innocence, and carrying the lost baskets and guns. Dick tossed them in front of the sportsmen. "We found these down in the cherry thicket. None of 'em's been fired so we figured you must have just forgot to bring 'em back with you. It's lucky Matt and I happened to be down that way, practicing our Comanche war whoops."

The disgruntled sportsmen slunk off. A day or two later they remembered urgent business back in St. Louis and joined a wagon train rolling east on the Platte Road. That night, in solemn ceremony, Dick and Matt were made honorary chiefs for ridding the post of the worst pest since lice were invented.

Dick's long spell of tedious peace and his profitable Ute trade ended simultaneously and abruptly. A large village of Utes had camped on the Purgatory River, only twenty miles or so below the Mexican border, and were anxious for trade. Dick got together a long train of goods and set out, taking along seven helpers, including a Shawnee Indian.

The Shawnee was an excellent addition to the crew except for one minor matter he had neglected to mention when signing on. A short time before, one of his relatives had lost his scalp to a Ute war party and consequently the Shawnee's feelings toward that tribe were anything but amicable.

They were within two miles of the Ute village when the explosive situation burst into violence. A lone Ute warrior rode out to greet them. Without a word the Shawnee shot him dead and tore off his scalp before Dick could reach him. There was no time for recriminations.

"Get the train turned around," Dick roared, "and head back for the Arkansas as fast as you can travel. The whole village will be swarming after us in no time and too itchy for scalps to listen to reason."

The shortest route back to Bent's Fort was to swing away from the river and make a beeline straight across the sand hills. It was in the midst of this desolate area without a rock or even a clump of greasewood for cover that the enraged Utes caught up. There were more than a hundred painted, howling savages against Dick and his seven companions. He had to think fast.

"Pull all the packhorses into a tight circle and cinch their lead ropes up close so they can't stampede and expose us. Even if they're knocked down they'll give us stout cover."

Luckily, almost half his trading stock consisted of powder and shot so they were free to fire as fast as they could reload. Like a majority of his race the Shawnee was an indifferent shot but the rest of Dick's party were crack marksmen and cool-headed veterans of many such clashes. They waited calmly behind their living barricade for the savage charge.

It came in a howling, thundering rush that split apart to flow past the beleaguered group on either side and come together into a tight circle of running ponies. Most of the Utes carried only bows and arrows, but Dick recognized a few of his own trade fusils and was thankful he had not done a bigger business with this particular band.

As the Utes swept past they loosed a volley of arrows and musket balls, most of which went wild. A few arrows and bullets thudded into the packs. One horse squealed and plunged with an arrow in its flank.

Then the rifles were answering and with almost every shot a saddle emptied or a pony went down. The Utes abruptly widened their circle to a more respectful distance. From here most of their arrows and musket balls fell short. Every few minutes an individual warrior would nerve himself to dash in for a closer shot, clinging to the offside of his pony for a shield. When he raised up to shoot, a rifle spoke with deadly accuracy.

At the end of an hour the sand was littered with dead or wounded Indians and horses and the number of solo charges had fallen off sharply. Only the Shawnee kept up a steady fire, shooting as fast as he could reload, with considerably more enthusiasm than skill.

Dick slashed open a pack and hauled out a half dozen of his trade fusils. He thrust these into the Shawnee's arms. "You got us into this mess. Now do something useful to get us out, instead of burning out your rifle barrel. Load these up so we'll have something to fall back on if they take a notion to charge."

A few of the Utes were still dashing around the circle, yelling and letting go wild shots. Most, however, had drawn together and were talking excitedly. Dick waited tensely, wondering if they were nerving themselves for a massed charge that would overwhelm the little group. Suddenly a number of Indians broke from the group and started forward, riding in pairs.

"Wait," Dick barked as the rifles steadied. "Hold fire for a minute. I think they're coming to pick up their dead and injured. If that's so, it means they've had about enough, unless we stir them up to fresh rage with more killing."

In a moment his guess was confirmed. Leaning down, each pair caught up a fallen comrade and dashed back, dragging the limp body between them. Dick counted fourteen dead or badly wounded Utes. At least twice that many ponies were down and a number of the Indians were riding double.

The circling and the howling and the harmless shooting continued for a time. Then abruptly the Indians came together, shook their weapons at the traders with a final yell of rage and frustration, and went streaming off in the direction of the Ute village.

In Dick's little group there were three or four arrow scratches and one minor wound from a spent musket ball. Miraculously, none of the horses had been killed or seriously injured. Dick looked at the Shawnee, squatting on his heels and happily admiring the Ute scalp. He opened his mouth to deliver a blistering lecture and then turned away with a hopeless shrug.

"What's the use?" he thought. "He'd never understand, and I suppose if I were in his skin, I'd have done the same thing."

So far, the price of that Ute scalp had been little more than a good scare. But this was only a first installment on the cost. The total payment through the months ahead would run considerably higher.

17

The most annoying thing about trouble with the Utes was the fact that all trails to Taos and Santa Fe led through country where they ranged widely. It was basic to Indian nature to hold all members of a group or tribe responsible for the acts of any one member. Consequently, as leader of the train, Dick was directly blamed for the killing of the Ute. In turn, this automatically made every white man a fair target for bloody retaliation. Mountain men suddenly found their casual junkets to the fleshpots of Taos fraught with peril unless they rode in strong force.

A week or two after the Ute's murder, Dick accepted the job of delivering important messages to the Taos store. He set out with two companions, eccentric old Bill Williams, the toughest man in the mountains, and Ed Walters, who had been part of Dick's earlier trapping brigades.

They encountered no Indians at all on the way down. The return trip was equally uneventful until an afternoon when they were riding through a rocky, thickly wooded canyon. Without warning a shot crashed from the underbrush by the trail. Walters, in the lead, yelled and threw up his arms. Dick spurred forward and caught him as he reeled in the saddle. "Steady, Ed. Do you think you can hang on until we're out of this trap?"

"I'll . . . try," the trapper gasped, white-faced.

Old Bill galloped alongside, shrilling, "Do 'ee har, now, Injuns is all about. Wagh! This child is for finding a place to cache up quick, afore we're out o' hoss and hair."

Bending low, with Dick supporting the reeling Walters, the trio raced up the canyon, followed by Indian howls and a swarm of arrow and musket balls. They burst out into open country and raced on, Bill watching their back trail. After several miles without a sign of pursuit they halted and lifted the wounded man down.

The wound was serious, but not as fearful as it had looked at first glance. The ball had struck the left hipbone and been deflected, glancing through Walters' body just under the skin and emerging from his right side. They dressed the wound as best they could and got him to Bent's Fort. Under the care of Dr. Hempstead, an Eastern physician who had recently taken up residence there, he recovered his health but never his enthusiasm for riding through hostile Indian country.

Meanwhile, his Ute trade dead, Dick was looking around for some other profitable venture. A sudden small but heartening upward jump in the price of beaver plews decided him. With Matt Curdy and three other trappers he headed back to the mountain streams of northern Colorado. They found beaver plentiful and by late fall the bales of plews on their pack mounts were close to capacity. There had been no Indian trouble and they were working southward again, planning to winter at Bent's Fort.

Late one afternoon they were breaking camp to move to a new location. While the last packs were being lashed, Dick rode out for a quick scout. It was more or less routine, but the habit of caution had become second nature and his sharp eyes missed nothing.

At the edge of a little brush-lined stream he glanced at the rushing water and stiffened. A freshly broken twig with its leaves still attached was drifting down the current. The normally crystal-clear water showed a faint muddiness. He sprang down and began working his cautious way upstream under cover of willow thickets. He had gone no more than two hundred yards when he saw a large force of mounted Indians crossing the stream, the hoofs of their ponies roiling the water. From their varied costumes and ornaments he recognized one of the most dreaded bands in the mountains. It was made up of renegade Shawnees, Arapahoes, and Blackfeet, criminal outcasts from their own tribes, who preyed on whites and Indians alike with inhuman ferocity.

Dropping back, Dick raced to the camp. "Indians are closing in. Mount up and follow me fast. I spotted a place this morning that will give us perfect cover."

With the packtrain prodded into a reluctant gallop, he led the way across two miles of open country to a natural fort, a great jumble of fallen rock at the base of a steep mountain slope. Here, among jagged masses higher than their heads, they picketed the train before selecting their own strong defense positions.

They were barely settled when the Indians appeared at a gallop, following the clear trail of their hasty flight. Dick let them get almost to the rocks before his first shot emptied a saddle to open the fight. Other rifles barked and the Indians fell back with yells of rage, leaving three bodies on the ground.

The conflict fell into a familiar pattern. The Indians fanned out to cover three sides of the rock mass, racing their ponies back and forth and howling their war cries. From time to time they dashed in close enough to send a storm of arrows and musket balls pattering among the rocks, then raced back out of range.

Each time the deadly mountain rifles took their toll and as the afternoon wore on the Indians' enthusiasm for such charges noticeably waned. To break the routine, the trappers began overcharging their rifles and picking off Indian ponies at extreme ranges. As dusk closed down the Indians sullenly withdrew, disappearing behind a distant ridge.

"They've had a bellyful of us, I'm thinkin'," Curdy exulted. "By now they've figgered we got enough extry supplies and ammunition in the packs to stand off an army for a week."

"I'm not so sure we might not have to yet, Matt," Dick said grimly. "They've also seen a lot of mighty fine horses and mules and peltry for the taking. I can't see 'em letting a puny handful of five men keep them from that rich plunder without making a harder try than this to put us under. We'll stay put right here until daylight and see how matters stand then."

The words were barely spoken when a thunderous crashing broke out up the steep slope at their backs. A full moon was up and by its light Dick could see an enormous mass of rock rolling and bounding down the slope directly toward them.

"Take cover," he yelled. "Squeeze into the deepest and narrowest slot you can find and protect your heads."

There was a concerted dive for shelter. Dick squirmed into a gap between rocks, shielding his face and head with his crossed arms.

The boulder struck the rocks somewhere behind him with a tremendous smash and an impact that jarred the earth. It broke apart, showering the whole area with fragments. Dick was pelted with bits too small to inflict damage but he could hear larger pieces crashing close by.

Almost before the rain of debris stopped falling, he was scrambling back to his perch, shouting, "Everybody who's able, back to your post and look sharp. They may attack while they think we're hurt or disorganized."

Then Matt Curdy's voice bawled, "Here they come!" and his rifle banged.

In the bright moonlight Dick could see a line of figures racing toward their stronghold. He began shooting as fast as he could reload, hearing the other guns barking steadily. The line of charging Indians wavered and fell back.

Presently a small fire bloomed in the distance. It was clearly a signal to other Indians up the mountain, because almost immediately the rumble of another rock avalanche sent the defenders diving back to deep cover. Crouching, Dick could hear great boulders strike and rebound to go crashing off down the canyon. The sound was reassuring, for it indicated that their own rock cover was not being demolished by the bombardment.

During lulls he could hear their horses and mules snorting and squealing, but whether from injuries or simply from fright he could not tell. By sheer luck they had been picketed at the very foot of a cliff whose slight overhang offered some degree of protection.

The nightmare pattern of attack continued. After each new rockfall the Indians made another probing advance that melted swiftly when the bang of mountain rifles showed the defenders still alive and alert. Each time Dick anxiously counted the reports, feeling a vast relief when he found all four of his companions still able to keep up the fire.

With the light of dawn the rock avalanches ceased and no follow-up attack came. As daylight came on they could see the Indians massed a mile or so away. Presently three riders left the group and cantered toward the rocks, blankets streaming in the dawn wind, their faces turning from side to side as they searched for signs of life. They halted a little way out, then came forward more warily. They were within a hundred yards of the rocks when three mountain rifles spoke as one and three riderless ponies raced off in wild panic.

The sight was too much for the surviving Indians. Without even attempting to recover the three bodies they wheeled and went streaming off, finally disappearing in the distance. This time there was no doubt that the attack was over for good.

Except for minor cuts and bruises from flying fragments, Dick's handful had suffered no casualties, nor had any of the horses and mules been struck. They pushed on immediately and wound up their trapping season without further incident.

They reached Pueblo in late January 1847, the air full of flying snow and a belated winter howling at their heels. Here they stopped a while to rest and get warm and catch up on the news of the Mexican War, which had barely begun when they left Bent's Fort.

"You didn't miss any excitement," Alex Barclay told them.

"Right after you left last fall, General Kearny came through with a pack of Missouri roughnecks he called an army. They marched down to Santa Fe and New Mexico surrendered without a shot being fired. He appointed Charles Bent governor and went on to take California. Things have been quiet ever since."

The other mountain men were all away and at Barclay's urging Dick and his companions hung around a few days, enjoying what meager hospitality the small fort could offer. Thus they were there the day a gaunt figure stumbled in, half frozen and reeling with exhaustion, his moccasins worn to shreds. It took Dick a moment to recognize a friend and fellow mountain man by the name of John Albert.

"All hell's broke loose in Taos," he gasped. "Charles Bent and the other Americans have been murdered and the mob's getting nerved up to come and wipe out Bent's Fort. I got away and come over the mountains on foot to get warning to them."

18

THE shocking news threw Pueblo into turmoil. The murder of Charles Bent stunned Dick with a deep sense of personal loss. The eldest Bent had been almost a second father, his encouragement and aid responsible in good part for all of Dick's successes in the West. The first shock of grief was followed by a tidal wave of fury.

With food and warmth and rest, Albert recovered sufficient strength to give them more details of the Taos massacre. The blood-crazed mob had been made up of Mexican peasants and Pueblo Indians, the former led by Pablo Montoya, the latter by Chief Tomás Romero. On the night of January 19th a mob of well over a thousand swarmed out to butcher every American and every Mexican who had been friendly to the conquerors.

Charles Bent, just arrived from Santa Fe to visit his family, was the first to be killed and his body savagely mutilated. Other victims included Sheriff Stephen Lee, District Attorney James Leal, and Prefect Cornelio Vigil. Two mountain men who had ridden in as the violence started managed to elude the mob.

One, Charles Towne, raced south to carry the grim news to Santa Fe. His companion, gravel-voiced Charley Autobeas, rode twelve miles north to Arroyo Hondo. At the distillery John Albert and eight other mountain men were enjoying Simeon Turley's hospitality and produce. Charley croaked his warning, then raced on toward Bent's Fort.

The ten men at the distillery had just time to bar the gate of the stockade when a mob of five hundred stormed the walls.

A fierce battle raged for two days and nights. On the third night, with half the defenders dead, the mob swarmed in. John Albert alone escaped in the darkness. Without coat or blanket, he had walked and run a hundred forty miles through the bitter cold to bring his warning.

"There's no knowing if Charley Autobeas got through to the fort," he finished. "Soon as I've rested a mite, I'll borry one o' your horses and ride on to Bent's myself."

Alex Barclay got up, grim-faced, and took his rifle from the wall. "If this is a general uprising, we've got the makings of another massacre right here. We employ fifteen Mexicans who could turn on us in a minute if they got wind of what's happening. Help me round them up before trouble starts."

With rifles cocked and torches flaring in the wind, they tramped along the row of workers' shanties outside the stockade, rousting out the startled and protesting Mexicans and their families. These were disarmed and locked in the fort's big storeroom. When the task was done Dick faced his companions.

"The last I heard, Colonel Sterling Price was still in Santa Fe with three companies of troops. If they weren't surprised and slaughtered the same way, they must be marching on Taos by now. He'll need every fighting man he can muster. You fellows can do as you please, but I'm heading down to give him a hand and settle a few scores."

"You ain't goin' alone, Dick," Matt Curdy said. "We all had good friends that went under down there. We're with you."

Four days of hard riding through deep snow and bitter cold brought them to the hills along the east side of the valley of Taos. It was immediately evident that no American forces had arrived as yet, since the towns swarmed with armed Mexicans and Indians.

"They're bound to show up soon," Dick said. "Our best bet is to camp up the mountains where we can be ready to slip down and join them for the fighting."

They found an ideal site, high on a shoulder of the Sangre

de Cristos, shielded by a dense growth of pine and cedar. From a high, rocky point they could look almost straight down into San Fernandez and three miles north to the Indian village of Taos. Here they settled down to watch and wait out the dragging days in angry impatience.

Then, on the late afternoon of February 2 they saw a ragtag horde of five or six hundred Indians streaming up the road from Santa Fe. Part of the mob camped at San Fernandez while the rest pushed on to Taos. Watching them, Curdy nodded with grim satisfaction. "They've tooken a whipping, and a hard one. Half of 'em's bandaged up and they've lost their gear."

Dick nodded agreement. "That means our troops must be right on their heels, Matt. We should be seeing action soon now."

They waited impatiently but darkness fell with no sign of the pursuit. All through the night fires blazed in the valley and Indian riders pounded back and forth between the towns.

Shortly after sunup a handful of mounted Indians raced into San Fernandez from the south. Their arrival was the signal for frenzied activity. The Indians snatched up their weapons and rushed off across the snow to Taos. A few Mexicans ran with them, but hundreds more fled from the town to take cover on the wooded slope of the mountain below the trappers' camp.

Curdy swore wrathfully. "They'll be the skunks who had a hand in the killings t'other night. Now they're skeered out of their wits at what's goin' to happen to 'em when our boys catch up."

Dick slammed an angry fist onto his knee. "Meantime they've got us cut off. That whole pack is swarming between us and the valley, Matt, all armed and crazy desperate. Even when our army comes, we'd never get through alive by daylight to join them. Whatever happens, we're trapped here until dark."

It was nearly noon before the American forces came into view far down the road, a pathetically small body of troops trailing a battery of field pieces and a line of supply wagons. As the column inched closer the reason for its slow progress became apparent. Of the four hundred and eighty men in Price's command, more than three hundred were on foot, stumbling with exhaustion after two hard-fought battles and twelve days of floundering through deep snow.

Then Dick caught sight of riders in buckskin and almost whooped aloud. "Look who's leading! It's Colonel St. Vrain with a big force of mountain men he rounded up in Santa Fe. Now we'll give those devils what they deserve."

They counted sixty familiar figures riding close-bunched ahead of the infantry. Not to be able to race down and join their friends and old comrades immediately was infuriating but they had no choice. Such an attempt without the cloak of darkness would be suicidal.

Price advanced warily, sending the mountain men ahead to search the buildings for ambuscades before entering the town. There was a brief rest for the weary troops while St. Vrain and a few of his men rode on and circled Taos, scouting its defenses. Then a bugle sounded and the column resumed its advance. From their high observation point, Dick and his companions could only watch in angry frustration and some apprehension.

Since daybreak they had seen bands of Indians coming down from the mountains to join those in Taos until they estimated the defense force as no fewer than seven hundred fighting men. While the village consisted of only three buildings, it was a formidable stronghold to attack.

Two of the buildings were great adobe pueblos seven stories high, each story set back slightly, leaving a narrow encircling balcony. Neither pueblo had doors or windows. Access was only through the roofs by means of ladders which the occupants drew up after them. The thick walls were pierced with rows of loopholes through which the defenders could fire without exposing themselves.

North of the pueblos stood the old adobe church of La Iglesia de Taos, even more massively constructed. It had no windows and only a single door on the south, but crude loopholes had been chopped through its outer walls. A thick wall of adobe brick reinforced with timbers joined the three buildings to form a rectangular stockade.

From their high vantage point, Dick could see a huge body of Indians in and around the church. The roofs and balconies of the pueblos were crowded, the ladders drawn up to thwart any storming party that might get past the outer walls.

"There'll be fight enough fer all of us, I'm thinkin'," Curdy said, "afore them red devils hollers quits. That is, unless them little popguns on wheels kin batter through them mud walls, which I misdoubt. They was mainly useful to make a big bang to scare Injuns with, but Pueblos don't scare wuth a dang. It'll be a hard, bloody job diggin' 'em out and it ain't goin' to be finished in one day, neither, to this hoss's mind."

His gloomy prediction was amply confirmed during the remaining hours of daylight. Halting his force beyond gun range of the wall, Price had his little battery wheeled up to the fore and unhitched. It consisted of one six-pounder cannon and three twelve-pounder howitzers whose high trajectory and low muzzle velocity made them all but worthless for battering down walls. This was quickly evident when the Americans opened fire.

The church, which was the strongest point and sheltered the heaviest concentration of Indians, was the target for the opening bombardment. The howitzers bellowed first, the smoke trails of their shells arching against the leaden clouds. The three shells burst against the wall with thunderous reports, throwing up great billowing clouds of smoke and adobe dust.

When the cloud lifted, even the watchers on the mountain could see that no damage had been inflicted. A shallow dimple had been gouged out of the surface but the thickly packed and dried adobe had turned the main force of the blast harmlessly outward.

A solid shot from the cannon struck at a slight angle and bounded off, leaving only a shallow furrow. Another volley of shells merely pitted the massive wall. A third, sent on a higher trajectory, only rebounded from the heavy roof timbers and burst in the air with no effect.

Price had the cannon wheeled closer and fired point-blank. The six-pound iron ball half buried itself in the adobe, hung for a moment, and then rolled out onto the ground below. A second shot, driven by a heavier powder charge, went through the wall but left only a round hole which the defenders promptly used as an additional gunport.

By this time the early winter twilight was closing down and the gun crews were reeling from exhaustion. Price had the guns hitched and the frustrated column plodded back to San Fernandez for the night. As they broke off the Indians swarmed out onto the walls and balconies to dance and jeer the enemy's failure.

Up on the mountainside, Dick and his companions stood by their horses, waiting impatiently for the last gray daylight to fade. He glanced across at Matt Curdy's set face. "You were right clear down the line, Matt. There'll be plenty of bloody work for all of us tomorrow."

19

Under cover of darkness the trip down the mountain was an anticlimax. They saw no sign of enemies and reached the camp of the mountain men without incident to receive a rousing welcome. St. Vrain, his granite face betraying his grief and fury, pumped Dick's hand.

"What news have you had of William and the people at the fort? The last word we had, a strong force of guerrillas had set out to raid our ranches and then attack the fort itself."

"We know even less than you about the situation. When we left Pueblo, John Albert was riding to Bent's Fort with a warning. Since then, we've been hiding up the mountain, completely out of touch."

While they warmed themselves and enjoyed their first hot food in more than a week, Dick and his companions heard what little was yet known of the uprising. In Santa Fe, Colonel Price had learned of the plot from friendly Mexicans and had jailed the ringleaders in time to prevent bloodshed. Near Mora a band of rebels struck a wagon train, killing eight Americans. Troops from Las Vegas, moving swiftly, had virtually demolished Mora, killing or capturing the entire force.

"We've handed them two bloody whippings on the way," Ceran said with cold satisfaction. "At La Cañada, twenty miles above Santa Fe, we ran into fifteen hundred Indians and Mexicans and scattered them like sheep. We killed at least thirty-six and took forty-five prisoners. Then at El Embudo we gave them an even worse beating. By then the Mexicans had their bellies full of fighting. Most of them deserted the Indians and ran off to hide in the hills. Once we've cleaned out this nest of rebels in Taos, the back of the uprising will be broken."

The tall, trim figure of Colonel Price came striding from the army camp. He saluted St. Vrain and nodded a greeting to Dick. "I'm concentrating tomorrow's assault on the church, which is their main stronghold. I'd like your men to cover the rear where the mountains come down to within a half mile of the pueblos, to cut off their escape when they start to run. This is to be a decisive whipping, with none getting away into the mountains to reorganize and stir up more trouble."

St. Vrain nodded acknowledgment. "You seem mighty certain they're going to run, Colonel."

Price's face set in grim lines. "One way or another we're going to breach that wall and come to grips with them tomorrow. When we do, I promise you that the ones still able to run will be running as fast as their legs can carry them."

In the cold gray light of morning the column moved out over the frozen slush of the plain, the men shivering in a raw north wind that brought the sound of defiant yelling from the village. As they drew closer they could see Indians crowding the top of the wall and the roofs of the pueblos, howling and shaking guns in the air. Dick cantered up beside St. Vrain.

"Colonel, while the foot soldiers are swinging around to attack from the west, what's wrong with our riding straight in and having us a bit of target practice? After all, there's nothing like a little ball of Galena to keep one of those murdering devils from busting away to the mountains."

"It's a fine idea, Dick, and one I was about to suggest myself." He hunched around in the saddle and raised his voice. "Anyone whose hands are cold is free to move up and warm them on a hot rifle barrel."

The mountain men needed no broader hint. Yelling like Comanches they kicked their mounts into a run and swept forward. Indian muskets set up a banging, the balls kicking up spurts of dirty snow. Then the mountain rifles were speaking, almost every shot finding its mark in the close-packed mass on the wall. Dick fired and saw a big Indian drop his musket and pitch down onto the snow. Howling and firing as fast as they could reload, the mountain men streamed around the east and north sides of the walled village. The Indians were ducking and scrambling back, leaving bodies along the top, with here and there a brown arm or leg dangling over the edge.

Meanwhile galloping teams were wheeling the fieldpieces into line four hundred yards west of the church. While the guns were being unhitched and loaded, Captain Burgwin's dismounted dragoons with a platoon of infantry moved forward and drove the Indians from the top of the west wall with a heavy and accurate fire.

From all sides Indians were tumbling off the walls and racing to take shelter in the church. In a moment a fierce and steady fire poured from the loopholes in the walls and a bugle called the skirmishers back out of range.

The artillery opened up with a thunderous crashing, while the echoes, rolling back from the surrounding mountains, magnified the din. One howitzer directed a steady hail of grapeshot against the pueblos, clearing the roofs and pinning the defenders inside. The other two, with the cannon, resumed their ineffectual pounding of the massive church wall.

Price ordered the battery moved up to a scant hundred yard range with little better effect. The shells still pitted the adobe without weakening it materially. Solid shot from the cannon went through but made only a round hole the size of the ball. He finally ordered the bombardment to be directed against the old timbered outside wall, just south of the church, with better results.

This connecting wall, built years before to repel raiding Comanches, Apaches, and Utes, was not as thick nor its adobe bricks as solidly packed. The reinforcement that was to have been its main strength proved to be its weakness. When a direct shot or shell-burst struck one of the massive timbers, the full length tore away, bringing whole sections of the weakened wall crashing down. By eleven o'clock a large gap had been opened below the corner of the church. With ammunition running low, Price halted the bombardment.

Presently a courier galloped out to St. Vrain with a request for a detail of sharpshooters to cover a storming operation. "If you have any marksmen who can put their shots through the loopholes, the Colonel would especially appreciate it."

St. Vrain smiled, "My men all had to be at least that good to stay alive. Tell the Colonel I'll send him twenty-five of the best."

Dick and Matt were among the select. While the mountain men poured a deadly fire against the loopholes, Captain Burgwin and Lieutenant Aubrey led assault details that gained the north and west walls of the church with only light casualties. Ducking under and between the loopholes, they set long ladders against the walls. Carrying armfuls of greasewood and other hot-burning brush, one group scrambled up and built hot fires on the wood roof. The timbers, ancient and sun-dried, quickly caught flame and began to burn furiously.

Meanwhile Captain Burgwin led a second detail, carrying a log battering ram, around through the gap in the wall to assault the heavy church door. They never reached it. While the guns had been breaching the wall, the Indians in the church had hurriedly chopped new loopholes around the door. Through these they met the assault party with a storm of point-blank fire.

Captain Burgwin fell, mortally wounded, and several others were hit too badly to carry on. The battering ram was dropped and the detail stumbled back, carrying the dying captain. Although sections of the roof were on fire, the battle was at a stalemate.

St. Vrain had ridden in to watch the assault and was standing by the sharpshooters. Colonel Price turned to him, his face set in grim lines. "This is maddening. There are four or five hundred Indians inside that building and we can't get at them."

"I know one way," Dick said to St. Vrain. "If a few of us with axes got up under those loopholes, we could chop through that mud in no time. It's no trick at all, as you know from changing those inside walls at the fort."

Price looked up sharply. "It wouldn't be a picnic, but if anyone wants to try there's a load of axes on the lead supply wagon."

Despite the hazards, there was a rush of volunteers for the attempt. Dick and Matt were among the thirty-five selected from both mountain men and troops. As they crouched, gripping axes and awaiting the order to charge, Dick turned to St. Vrain. "Colonel, you'd better be ready for action back on the other side pretty quick now. We're going in, and when we do there are bound to be a few of 'em coming out."

Then the bugle blared and they were running, bent low and zigzagging, charging into a storm of musket fire. The air was filled with the hiss and hum of flying lead. A ball tore into the slack of Dick's hunting shirt with a jerk that spun him half around. A few yards away a man grunted and fell, the ax flying from limp hands. Another went to his knees and got up again, to stumble on, limping.

Nevertheless they reached the church with only three men killed and a handful with minor wounds. Crouching below and between the loopholes, safely out of range of the defenders' guns, they began swinging the axes against the wall.

Dick and Matt chopped furiously to deepen and enlarge a gouge left by a shell burst. At every stroke the dry adobe mud crumbled and clouds of choking yellow dust roiled up to mingle with black powder smoke belching from the loopholes. Over their heads a loophole spurted smoke and fire. Matt Curdy swore and slapped at his neck as a shred of burning bullet patch drifted down.

Suddenly Dick's ax broke through, the momentum of his blow throwing him off balance. He caught himself and fell back an instant before a burst of fire converged on the hole from inside. As it slacked off, their axes swung again. Alternately striking and dodging back, they opened a hole roughly two feet in diameter. Efforts to widen it further met such a hot fire from the defenders that they had to desist.

"That's about it," Matt said. "There must be five hundred Injuns inside and not a hundred of 'em can be close enough to shoot. The rest of 'em are prob'ly loading guns and handing 'em forward as fast as their friends can empty them."

A courier came dodging up through the dust and smoke. "Colonel Price says we've only solid shot for the cannon to shoot point-blank, but if you'll pull back he'll try to depress the howitzers enough to drop shells against the holes from outside."

"Wait," Dick said sharply. "I've got a better idea. Tell him to send us over some of the shells with the fuses cut short. We'll light them and throw them in by hand. That way we can be sure they'll explode where they're needed most."

The courier gave him a startled look and scrambled away. Presently men came running, carrying sacks of the twelve-pound explosive shells. Matt got out a Mexican cigar and his patent lighter, a metal tube full of cotton with a striker for flint at the tip. He puffed his cigar alight and doused the lighter by closing the tube with his finger until the sparks were out.

"Dick," he shouted above the tumult of gunfire and yelling, "I didn't much take to bein' out there in the open with all them Injuns shootin' at me, but I can tell you one thing: I'd a dang sight ruther be out there than inside when these things start goin' off."

"Maybe," Dick said, "you'd rather have been in Charles Bent's doorway where they cut him down and hacked him to pieces, or out in the street where they dragged James Leal naked and scalped him alive. Or maybe in the barn where they caught those two boys, Narciso Beaubien and Pablo Jaramillo, and jabbed them to death slowly."

"I'd ruther be right here," Matt said, holding out his glowing cigar. "Light up and start tossing, Dick."

The short fuse sputtered, throwing out a shower of sparks. Dick held it a moment, watching its gray length shorten, then hurled it through the hole. It burst almost at once with a muted thunder that was echoed by the crash of other shells being tossed in along the line. Dick sent in two more as fast as he could light them, then snatched up his ax to attack the hole with new fury. As the blasts died away he could hear the groans and cries of the wounded inside. In that close-packed horde the shells must have wrought fearful havoc, but there were plenty of Indians still able to resist. A renewed storm of fire from inside drove the attackers back from the holes before any could be enlarged greatly.

The courier came scrambling back. "Colonel Price's compliments on a fine piece of work, gentlemen. Now if you'll stand back, he'll finish your job with the cannon."

The six-pounder was already being hauled and manhandled up to point-blank range opposite the hole they had started. Most of the surviving Indians had been driven back from the west side of the building by the deadly shell bursts and only a few scattered shots came from the loopholes.

The gun opened fire, the crew carefully placing their shots in a vertical row along the edge of the opening. At the tenth shot the whole side collapsed, leaving a breach wide enough for a man to duck through. A wild, hoarse cheer went up from the Americans and the whole force surged forward in a race to reach the opening.

The first man into the breach ran into murderous fire and went down, literally riddled with shots. Those behind him leaped over the body and poured in, yelling crazily and firing at shadowy figures dimly seen through the smoke and dust.

Dick whirled away. "Come on, Matt. Let's get our horses and get around to our crowd fast. Any minute now the Indians who are still on their feet will break for the mountains."

They had barely reached their tethered horses when the panic in the village began. As they swung into their saddles they could see Indians swarming down ladders or jumping from the lowest tier of the pueblos. Then the church door burst open and

141

survivors of that carnage came streaming out, running in blind terror toward the gate and the haven of the mountains beyond.

Half the church roof was ablaze, sending a great column of black smoke up against the leaden sky. A soldier—Private Jim Quinn of Illinois, a cousin of Stephen A. Douglas—had scrambled up a ladder and was nailing an American flag to the corner. In the open plaza soldiers and Indians were locked in hand-to-hand battles.

Dick and Matt swept around the north side of the wall at a dead run onto a scene of wild and terrible vengeance. The whole plain was covered with fleeing Indians and pursuing mountain men. Every figure in buckskin rode with the memory of close friends tortured and mutilated and there was no thought of quarter in any mind.

They saw Jim Beckwourth ride down a fleeing Pueblo, split his skull with a tomahawk, and race on after another. The snow was already dotted with bodies. Here and there knots of Indians had gathered to make a desperate stand and little fights raged until the mountain rifles took their inevitable toll.

Matt Curdy whooped and went pounding off in pursuit of a running figure. Before Dick could follow an arrow hummed past his face so close he felt the wind of its feathers. He whirled to see brown figures behind a row of bushes that lined one of the *acequias*—the shallow irrigation ditches that crisscrossed the valley floor.

The rifle flew to his shoulder and jolted. An Indian with a musket pitched out of the bushes onto his face. A second burst out and fled across the snow, trying to fit an arrow to his bow as he ran. He tried to turn and shoot without breaking stride and tripped over a rock. The arrow went wild as he fell sprawling, grabbing for another shaft. Dick rode over him, leaning down to fire his pistol into the savage face in passing.

As swiftly as it had begun, the fight petered out. A handful of Indians reached the safety of the mountains but behind them they left fifty-one bodies scattered across the valley. Another hundred lay in and around the church. It was truly, as President Polk later said in Washington, "one of the most signal victories which has been gained during the war."

Dick and Matt joined St. Vrain and a couple of others on the ride back across the crimsoned snow to the village. There was little talk. Exhaustion and the letdown after the strain of battle gripped them all. Ahead, the figure of an Indian lay crumpled on the snow, a big man, well over six feet and powerfully built. St. Vrain suddenly reined in sharply.

"Hold on! I know that devil well. He's Big Todo, one of the leaders of the massacre. I've been told he took a hand in killing Charles and several of the others." He swung from the saddle, his face grim. "I want to make sure this one is really dead and not just shamming."

The Indian lay face down, his right hand under his body. St. Vrain hooked the toe of his moccasin under the brown shoulder and started to roll the body over. With the speed of a striking snake the big Pueblo shot to his feet, gripping a steel-tipped arrow that had been concealed under his chest.

He lunged at St. Vrain, throwing him off balance, driving the arrow at his throat. Ceran caught the brown wrist, turning the blow aside, forcing the Indian's hand back with all the power of his own considerable strength. His right hand closed on the other wrist and the two stood chest to chest, straining with all their might in equal contest.

At the first move, Dick was out of his saddle, yelling, "Hold him, Ceran, until I get behind." At such close quarters a pistol shot could endanger St. Vrain and a knife thrust might miss the heart.

Dick snatched his hatchet and leaped to get behind the big Pueblo. The Indian planted his feet and swung St. Vrain in a circle, keeping his body toward Dick as a shield. Matt and the other two were jumping down to take a hand. Dick was circling, his tomahawk poised, but St. Vrain's body was always between him and the foe.

Abruptly Dick stopped, reversed his field and darted the opposite way. Big Todo tried to follow the move but St. Vrain's powerful muscles held him for the moment it took Dick to get behind. The ax blade struck with a hollow, ringing *thunk*. St. Vrain let go and jumped back as the huge figure collapsed in a limp sprawl.

Dick bent over it, then straightened. "This time," he said, "he isn't fooling anybody but himself."

20

The battle had cost the Americans seven dead and forty-five wounded, and the victory was still not complete. Staring up at the twin pueblos, looming silent and formidable in the dusk, Price said grimly, "There must be three to four hundred Indians holed up in there yet, without a door or window that could be forced. If they won't come out, we'll have to go in after them the same way we did today."

They were breakfasting in the cold dawn, bracing themselves for a new assault, when Dick jumped to his feet and pointed. "We can relax, boys. It looks like our war is over."

Streaming out from the village was a procession of weeping women and children carrying white flags. As they approached the camp they fell on their knees, wailing for mercy. The surviving chiefs and warriors in the pueblos wanted no more fighting.

"Very well," Price told the interpreter. "We will accept their surrender on one condition. Tell them we mean to try and punish everyone, Indian or Mexican, who had a hand in the Taos murders. If they want peace, they must hand over any guilty ones with them now and help us run down any who got away."

The weeping band plodded back with their message while the Americans waited tensely, ready to resume the attack if the offer was rejected. At last they saw ladders being let down and a horde of Indians swarmed from the pueblos. They came across the snow, driving two bound figures before them.

Colonel Price let out his breath and drove an exultant fist into his palm. "We've won. That's Pablo Montoya, the Mexican devil who planned the uprising and led the massacre, and Tomás Romero, who brought the Indians into it. He's the one they say scalped Governor Bent with his own hand. Getting hold of those two puts an end to the uprising for good."

Sullen and silent, the two captives were locked in the tiny *calabozo* while preparations were made for an immediate military trial. While a parade of curious soldiers came to gape at the prisoners, Dick and Matt hunkered in the shade across the plaza to decide future plans.

Suddenly from the jail came the sound of a pistol shot, followed by a tumult of yelling and scuffling. Dick and Matt ran across and jammed their way in far enough to see the body of the Indian Romero, on the dirt floor. Soldiers were pinning the arms of a private by the name of Fitzgerald, one of Captain Burgwin's dragoons.

"What happened?" Matt asked.

"Fitz shot him," a jail guard said. "He come wantin' to see the prisoner and then he snatched out his gun and shot him dead."

Colonel Price came crowding in to hear the details and ordered Fitzgerald confined under heavy guard in one of the stout adobe huts. "He'll have to stand trial for murder, regardless of the character of his victim."

"They'd oughta pin a medal on him," a soldier beside Dick growled. "I'd have done the same in Fitz's boots. His brother was tortured and killed with the Texas-Santa Fe Expedition. Then yesterday he saw Cap'n Burgwin shot down and his best friend killed storming the church. I guess it preyed on his mind until he couldn't stand it no more."

"Poor devil," Dick said, his voice unusually loud. "It's too bad he didn't escape, but it's too late now. These adobe huts are mighty stout—except for the roof, which is only a thin shell of brush and mud."

Fitzgerald looked up sharply. His glance flicked to the low ceiling and was instantly veiled. Back outside, Matt said softly, "Dick, you done that apurpose, tellin' him how to bust out, come night."

"Maybe I did, Matt. Somehow it doesn't seem right to jail a fellow for doing what we were all doing yesterday."

Some time that night Fitzgerald broke through the flimsy roof of his prison and escaped. No one was greatly upset and there was only a brief token pursuit. The victors had more important matters to occupy their attention.

With the help of eyewitnesses, many of them friendly Mexicans, Colonel Price had compiled a list of those who had taken an active part in the Taos uprising. Dick was appointed marshal of Taos with the task of rounding up the guilty for trial.

The task proved remarkably easy. Dick already knew about where a horde of fugitives from San Fernandez had gone into hiding at the approach of the troops. Leading a detail of mountain men and soldiers, he swept the woods on the lower slopes east of town and quickly captured eighty of the wanted men.

U.S. Attorney Frank Blair came up from Santa Fe to handle the prosecution in a series of swift trials that were little more than a formality. Montoya and fourteen others were sentenced to hang for having an actual hand in the murders. Most of the rest received varying sentences for their part in the looting and destruction of American property. The first hangings were set for Friday, February 9, 1847, but Dick was not on hand for the grisly spectacle.

On Wednesday a courier rode in from El Paso with a message from Colonel Alexander Doniphan, commanding the First Missouri Volunteers. The colonel had met Dick at Bent's Fort the previous summer and been deeply impressed. "If I ever need a scout, Wootton, you're the one I'll send for."

"Any time, Colonel," Dick told him impulsively. "Just say the word and I'll be there."

Now Doniphan wrote to remind him of that promise. "The

First Missouri has been ordered south to join General Wool's force for an attack on Chihuahua. Your services as scout and guide urgently needed. Will expect you to join us posthaste. We march from El Paso February 8."

Within the hour Dick was pounding south toward new adventures and new country, feeling the familiar lift of excitement stir his blood. Pushing to the limit of endurance, he covered nearly three hundred and fifty miles in four days to catch up with the expedition below El Paso.

Doniphan's column consisted of eight hundred infantry, six field guns, and a train of two hundred baggage wagons. These were driven by prominent traders and merchants from frontier towns and posts. Their elected major was Sam Owens, a leading merchant from Independence whose half sister Mary had almost married a gawky Illinois lawyer by the name of Abe Lincoln. They all knew Dick and gave him a rousing welcome, with an invitation to camp with them apart from the troops.

"I'll do that and gladly," Dick said, shaking hands. "But I'm a mite surprised to see all you fellows leave your business to traipse down here."

"We didn't have much choice," Owens said wryly. "Doniphan commandeered all our wagons. About all we could do was to come along and keep an eye on our property."

Dick found the big colonel struggling to shape an army out of a pack of rowdy and rebellious Missouri farm boys whose appalling ignorance was exceeded only by their contempt for authority. Adding to his problems was a desperate shortage of ammunition and supplies.

"We need fresh meat," he told Dick, "but the only game we've seen are herds of wild cattle. The men shot up half our powder banging away at them until I put a stop to it. Then they tried lassoing the cattle and got themselves gored and trampled."

Dick quickly organized the job along the lines of his professional buffalo hunts for Bent's Fort. A few of the best shots rode down a herd and dropped only enough cattle for immediate need while a butchering crew followed up with wagons. The flesh was tough and stringy but it was meat and it restored their strength and spirits miraculously.

They had seen no enemy but the air was thick with rumors. Each day the jittery column fully expected to be ambushed by Mexican troops or, more terrifying, by Apache Indians. Dick's main task was to ride ahead with a small detail and scout the countryside for sign of hostiles. He also located waterholes, marked the safest and easiest wagon routes, and picked the next campsite. By working always a day's march ahead, he could tell Doniphan each night exactly what hazards and obstacles to anticipate the next day.

But despite his best efforts, the unruly pack managed to bumble itself into a succession of mishaps. One morning they ignored his trail markers and led the wagon train into a morass of quicksand. A day was wasted getting out the teams and most of the wagons. Some had to be abandoned. Others were extricated only by jettisoning their precious loads, including four tons of flour, almost their entire supply.

A few nights later their carelessness set off a raging prairie fire. A sudden change of wind drove it back on the camp and they spent the whole night fighting to save their remaining wagons and equipment from the flames.

At Ojo Caliente the obstreperous crowd took over an abandoned hacienda and refused to march until they had spent a day sporting in the hot springs. When Doniphan tried to order them on, a lanky corporal shouted: "Where do you come off tellin' us what to do? Maybe you forget that we *elected* you colonel and we kin *dis*-elect you any time we feel like it."

As they drew closer to Chihuahua, Dick began to see Mexican horsemen spying on them from the distant hills. There was little doubt that the long-delayed clash with the enemy might take place at any time and there were no signs of General Wool's forces approaching from the east to join them.

Then one morning, scouting far ahead, Dick found the Mexican Army, fifteen miles north of Chihuahua where the only road to the capital crossed the Sacramento River. Here, in a wide pass through the hills the governor of the state, Angel Trias, had a rancho with a large walled hacienda and stockaded corrals.

Mexican General Conde, a trained engineer, had converted this into a strong fortress with outlying works that commanded every foot of the road through the pass. The stout walls bristled with heavy cannon. Commanding the stronghold was General Heredia with more than four thousand troops.

From a lookout point on a nearby ridge, Dick saw columns of mounted dragoons dashing and wheeling in perfect order. In front of the fortress, lines of infantry drilled with the precision of veterans. When he slipped away at last to report, his eyes were bleak.

Colonel Doniphan listened to his report in thoughtful silence. "It sounds like a tough nut to crack all right, but if General Wool doesn't show up, we'll just have to crack it ourselves. We're too short of supply to turn back or sit here half the winter waiting for reinforcements."

Dick was appalled. He waved back toward the disorganized column, straggling in all directions without the faintest semblance of formation. "B-but, those are trained soldiers manning those works. You can't even make that bunch out there stay in line or go where you tell them."

Doniphan grinned faintly. "Dick, there's one thing you've still to learn about Missouri plowboys. They're a pack of unwashed roughnecks who won't take orders, won't drill, and don't know beans from buckshot about most matters. But when there's fighting to be done, I wouldn't trade 'em for all the fancy-dress drill teams on the continent. You wait and see, boy."

While the column straggled and whooped and horseplayed on toward the point of inevitable collision, Dick spent most of his days watching the Mexican fortifications. Nothing he saw gave him any marked upsurge of optimism over the outcome of a battle.

The Mexicans were well aware of the size and disorder of the approaching enemy and their own confidence soared to fantastic heights. Great crowds were pouring out from Chihuahua, setting up grandstands on the heights overlooking the field of battle. A band of Apaches camped on a nearby hill, ready to throw in with whichever side was winning for a share of scalps and plunder. Hot-eyed Mexican patriots had donated a thousand new ropes to be used for dragging captive gringos on a victory march to Mexico City.

On the afternoon of February 27, the column went into camp almost within sight of the enemy stronghold. Doniphan rode on with Dick and most of the traders for a look at the Mexican defenses. The swarming crowds of spectators, the brilliant uniforms of the dragoons and the bright flags whipping in the wind gave the scene a carnival atmosphere.

"It looks like a mighty strong place to force," Doniphan commented at last after long and thoughtful study. "I suppose the military textbooks would call it a natural, since the only road to Chihuahua runs through that pass and under their guns."

"And they've had plenty of time to sight in those guns, too," Dick said grimly. "I watched their artillery practice and they've got that whole roadway so thoroughly covered a jackrabbit would be spattered trying to get through."

"That's interesting," Doniphan murmured. "With all their batteries trained on the road, I kind of wonder what they'd do if we were to swing off and follow that ridge over there around onto their flank."

Dick's jaw dropped. "I'll be dogged. I hadn't thought of that. All I could see was us on the road, marching right into their gunfire."

Doniphan chuckled. "I wouldn't be too surprised if they hadn't thought of it either. Well, comes morning we'll find out quick enough."

21

I<small>N THE</small> first light of dawn the American advance got under way. Sitting on his horse with Colonel Doniphan and his staff, Dick could only gape in amazement at the miraculous change in the Missouri wild men. There was none of the usual skylarking or malingering. They fell in like veterans, responding to orders with snap and at least a semblance of precision. For the first time he glimpsed the underlying strength of men to whom war was not a glorious career but a brief and necessary interruption to normal existence.

Where the road widened toward the broad pass, an order was barked and the column swung into a new and unorthodox formation. The wagons rolled up into four parallel columns with the troops and artillery between them, shielded on both sides from possible flank attack.

It was a maneuver long familiar to traders who used it on dangerous stretches of the Santa Fe trail. In case of attack, the columns could swing quickly into a tight hollow square, the heavy wagons forming a stout fortress. Thus shielded, they could hold off the Mexicans as easily as the trading caravans repelled Indian attacks.

In his days of careful watching, Dick had noted the maximum range of the Mexican cannon. Now, almost to that critical point, with eager Mexican gunners poising their matches to open the slaughter, Doniphan shouted a command. The columns wheeled smartly left, off the road, and up a gentle slope toward a low ridge that rimmed one side of the pass.

On a stretch of level ground beyond cannon range, the wagons swung into their defensive formation. The six field guns were run out and unhitched for action. The troops swarmed up the side of the ridge and advanced in line of battle toward the Mexican eastern flank.

The unexpected maneuver threw the Mexican force into stunned confusion. On the walls, a milling mob was trying to lever their heavy guns around to bear on the new and wholly unanticipated direction of attack. Along the flank some two thousand Mexican troops had been placidly waiting for their guns to finish smashing the column down on the road so they could charge down and annihilate the survivors.

Now suddenly they faced a solid wall of enemies, unhurt and eager for battle. The surprise threw their lines into chaos. Officers yelled conflicting orders and companies became hopelessly entangled in their attempts to face the unexpected charge.

The Missourians hit the milling mob and drove it back in wild confusion. At the same time, Doniphan's artillery opened up to make a shambles of Conde's elaborate fortifications. The American shells proved to have a disgracefully high percentage of faulty fuses. Some were duds while others burst harmlessly in midflight, but the ones that exploded on target did fearful damage.

Then some of the Mexican cannon got into action, bombarding the Missourians on the slope of the ridge. What could have been a bloody slaughter turned out to be a comic opera farce. The Mexican gunpowder was of such inferior quality that they were barely able to reach the slope at all. They had only solid shot and the balls were clearly visible as they struck and bounded along the ground.

The whooping farm boys turned the bombardment into a noisy game of "chicken," betting on who would be the last one to step aside from an oncoming shot. The only American casualties of the furious cannonade were a couple of stray horses that wandered in front of the bounding balls.

The Mexican troops were resisting courageously as they fell back but the initial error had disorganized their whole plan of battle and their leadership, like their gunpowder, was of poor quality. Nevertheless their desperate fight had slowed the initial charge of Doniphan's troops to a stubborn crawl.

While the fighting went on, a column of Mexican dragoons moved out and prepared to charge the Missourians. With flags waving and brilliant green and scarlet uniforms making a bright splash of color, they wheeled into line for the charge. But their horses, frightened by the noise of battle, were hard to control and the commanding officer insisted on waiting to dress a perfect line.

He was still dashing up and down, screaming orders, when one of Doniphan's gunners lobbed a shell into the center of the line. Men and horses flew in every direction and the survivors stampeded back to the crumbling shelter of the fortifications.

As a civilian employee, Dick had been ordered to stay behind with the traders, watching the battle from the tops of the wagons. None of them was happy with the passive role of spectator. Every man clutched his mountain rifle and squirmed with an unscratchable itch to use it.

"Dick," Sam Owens growled as they stood on the seat of his wagon, "I've had about enough of this. The colonel grabbed our wagons and drug us down to this godforsaken country. Bein' it's Army doin's, we'll very likely never see a cent of the pay he promised. That I kin put up with, but I'm dogged if I'm gonna let him keep me out of all the action."

"I feel the same way," Dick said. "I'm for jogging up forward and getting in a few shots before we forget how." He broke off with a joyous whoop. "Never mind, Sam. The Mexicans felt sorry for us so they're sending a special treat to keep us from feeling left out of the fun."

A force of some eight hundred to a thousand Mexican regulars had been posted on the west side of the pass. Now these were streaming down and across the road, bent on flanking the wagon train and artillery and striking Doniphan's lines from behind.

Dick's yell alerted the rest of the two hundred veteran frontiersmen. With shouts of glee and ringing war whoops, they dived to shelter behind their wagons. Mountain rifles began to crash and the front ranks of charging regulars melted under the murderous fire. Those behind fell over their bodies and the whole charge broke in panic and confusion. A volley from smoothbore muskets fell far short, while the rifles continued to take their deadly toll. The regulars faced the slaughter for gallant minutes and then broke. Leaving close to a hundred dead and wounded in front of the wagons, they fled wildly up the slope toward the half-ruined fortifications.

The sight proved irresistible to the traders, who came out in howling pursuit, loading and firing as they ran. The artillerymen caught the spirit of the chase. Yelling like demons, they swung their guns around and followed, dragging the heavy pieces across the field by brute strength.

Doniphan saw the fleeing foe and bawled an order for four companies of his troops to join the pursuit. The whole regiment jumped up as one man and charged up the hill toward the stronghold above. Officers and couriers jumped off their horses and joined the pell-mell charge, snatching up rocks and chunks of broken branches for weapons.

A gawky Missourian came galloping up the slope, waving an ax handle. Doniphan caught him by the arm and yelled above the din, "Stay back and hold the horses, private. That's an order."

"Go to hell!" the farm boy howled, jerking his arm loose. "I didn't jine the army to hold horses."

He raced on and Doniphan, pistol in hand, could only follow.

Up on the hilltops the mass of spectators had been stunned by the incredible turn of the battle. The sight of the massed charge broke their paralysis. Screaming in panic, men, women, and children stampeded into flight. Blind with terror, hundreds of them poured down across the field, colliding with their own soldiers and the pursuing Americans. The hillside became a hopeless tangle of troops and hysterical civilians.

Doniphan's men were reaching the battered fortifications, leaping over the rubble to attack the defenders with guns, knives, clubs, rocks, and bare fists. Dick and Sam Owens, racing shoulder to shoulder, fought their way through the screaming tangle and reached the stronghold. Somewhere on the ruined walls a Mexican gun banged and Sam Owens fell, shot through the head, one of the only two Americans killed in that incredible battle.

By the time Dick got to the wall, surviving Mexicans were fleeing in every direction, pursued by howling Missourians. A number reached the higher hills where the waiting Apaches enjoyed a Roman holiday of slaughter and scalp-taking.

The battle was ended, the last shot fired, by the time evening shadows crept over the scene of carnage. The known Mexican toll was three hundred and four killed and at least five hundred wounded. The American loss was two killed and seven wounded, none severely.

Their spirits finally tamed by sheer exhaustion, the Missourians went into camp around the wagons. With the back of Mexican resistance shattered, there was little fear of counterattack. Fifteen miles to the south lay the capital city of Chihuahua, defenseless and ready to be occupied the next day.

Dick had finished his supper and was drowsily looking forward to seeing the famous Mexican city when a summons from Doniphan brought him awake. He found the colonel hunched close to a blazing fire, writing dispatches.

"Dick, it's imperative that I get a full report of the battle back to Headquarters in Santa Fe as quickly as possible. I don't know of anyone else I could depend on to get through in a hurry. Will you undertake the mission?"

Dick sighed regretfully. "I'd figured on seeing the sights of Chihuahua tomorrow, Colonel, but if it's that all-fired important, I'll try my best to get through. I'll get me a bit of rest and leave an hour or two before dawn."

"Fine," Doniphan said in obvious relief. "By now there are likely to be both Mexicans and Apaches watching our back trail, figuring to grab any couriers we send back. Just tell me how many men you'll want to take to fight them off."

"Colonel," Dick said, "in the mountains they figure a man's worth by how many fights he avoids, not how many he survives. If it's all the same to you, I'd rather travel alone. I can always hide myself but I couldn't always hide a bunch of soldiers. Just give me a spare horse to carry forage and a little grub and I'll go it alone. Traveling at night and not building a fire, I ought to be able to get through first-rate."

The nine days it took him to reach the first U.S. Military Post at Albuquerque were among the most grueling of his life. To avoid the beaten road left by the column on its march south, he kept to the mountains, traveling mainly by night and living on hardtack and jerked beef. He made it through without once being spotted, although he frequently saw bands of Mexicans and Indians in the valleys below.

In the late evening of the ninth day he reached the Rio Grande opposite Albuquerque and faced a new and unexpected hurdle. The river was in full flood and far over its banks. The normal shallow crossing, a treacherous network of quicksand beds at best, was buried under a raging torrent.

There was nothing for it but to set his horses loose and attempt to wade and swim across. Already chilled and exhausted from the long ride, he was almost paralyzed by the stabbing cold of the icy water. Several times in the shallows he felt himself sinking into quicksand, but by swimming and threshing violently he tore himself free and struggled on.

It was pitch-dark when he finally reached the high bank on the east shore. With his last strength he clawed out and got hold of a bush growing from the loose mud. Tugging cautiously he began to pull himself up.

Suddenly, just over his head, a nervous voice croaked, "Halt! Who g-goes there? G-give the countersign or I'll sh-shoot."

Swept downstream by the fierce current, Dick had reached the shore beneath the army post. Through chattering teeth he managed to gasp, "I'm a messenger from Colonel Doniphan's forces at Chihuahua with dispatches for Santa Fe. Give me a hand quick, before this bush tears out and I'm swept away."

"You got to give the countersign," the sentry yelled. "I got my orders to shoot anybody that tries to cross without it."

"You half-witted knothead!" Dick raged. "I've been traveling for nine days. Where would I learn the countersign. Hurry up and get me ashore before I freeze to death."

"Stay right there," the sentry squawled. "If you so much as look over the bank, I'll blow your head off." He turned his head and began bawling, "Officer of the Guard! Officer of the Guard! Come quick!"

Dick felt a paralysis creeping over his muscles. The bush was slowly but steadily pulling loose from the bank. After what seemed an eternity, he heard pounding footsteps and a new voice took up the ridiculous questioning.

Eventually they pulled him out and half carried him to headquarters where the sealed dispatches inside his buckskins confirmed his story. After his first square meal and night's rest in nine days, Dick got a horse and pushed on to Santa Fe where he delivered his dispatches and formally terminated his army employment.

"Why not stay on with the army here, Wootton?" the officer asked. "We can keep you more than busy scouting and carrying messages."

Dick shook his head. "Sorry, sir, but I'm heading back to Taos right away. Now that the troubles are over, I've made up my mind to open a trading post. A place like that, handy to Santa Fe and the mountains, is bound to grow up fast and rich."

"You'd better not try that trip alone. Both the Utes and the Apaches have taken the warpath against the whites and that whole country between here and Taos is swarming with hostiles. We'll be sending a detachment of troops up in a day or two and the job of guiding them is yours if you'll wait over."

For a moment Dick was tempted to accept, but impatience was pushing him. In the lonely hours of the long ride up from Chihuahua he had had little to think about but his own situation and to take stock of his past and his future. Eleven years had slipped by since that fateful day when he boarded the *Yellowstone* for a quick look at the West. They had been good years, exciting and adventurous years, but they had trickled out through his fingers like grains of sand, leaving nothing permanent.

He had come West at the age of twenty with nothing but the clothes on his back, a few dollars in his pocket, and his rifle. Now, at thirty-one, he could still count his possessions as the clothing on his back, a few more dollars, and his rifle.

Around him a familiar world was slowly but surely dying, trampled to death under the boots of westering white men. The old carefree, rootless existence of the mountain man was vanishing forever. It was time—and past time—for a fellow to settle down and start building a solid and substantial future.

He squared his shoulders and shook his head. "Thanks all the same, sir, but I'm already late. I reckon I'll just push on by myself and take my chances."

Once more the fabulous Wootton luck rode with him—or perhaps what passed for luck was no more than an ingrained instinct for caution. He kept well off the traveled trails and saw no hostiles until he was within a dozen miles of Taos.

As always when he had to leave cover and cross open ground in daylight, he spent a long time studying the surrounding terrain before showing himself. Again that caution paid off.

Crouching in the underbrush at the Taos crossing of the Rio Grande, he looked across a broad clearing to the bushes on the far side. He could see no movement, no sign of life anywhere, yet some vague feeling of danger held him back from exposing himself. He continued to crouch in his cover, silent and motionless as a statue, while a full half hour dragged by.

Without warning, the bushes across the clearing suddenly parted and a band of forty painted and heavily armed Ute warriors rode into view. Dick's breath slid noiselessly out of his lungs. Beyond doubt, the Utes had been watching the clearing from the other side for at least as long. Only his uncanny sixth sense and his patience had kept him from stepping out and into their clutches.

As silent as a drifting shadow, Dick fell back to a safe distance and made a wide circle around the clearing. He reached his destination late in the afternoon of the third day without further incident.

On the following day a large and well-armed party from Santa Fe, coming over the same route, stumbled into a Ute ambush and several of their number were killed.

22

In the few weeks Dick had been away, the whole valley of Taos had undergone incredible changes. The U.S. War Department had established a major army post at San Fernandez de Taos, now known simply as Taos. In addition to a large permanent garrison, troops on their way to the theaters of war in central Mexico were held there for varying periods. It was also to be the outfitting point and jumping-off place for a number of major military expeditions into the Far West.

Most of the Americans originally in business in the valley had fortunately been away at the time of the uprising. They had escaped the massacre but their property had been plundered and wrecked by the mob. With Price's resounding victory, they all rushed back to rebuild and expand their establishments. At Arroyo Hondo Turley's mill and distillery were back in limited operation. St. Vrain had established a new distillery at Waipete Pueblo. Like Dick, he foresaw the end of the fur trade era and was putting down more permanent roots.

On the heels of the old-timers came a flood of new traders, merchants, suppliers, and contractors. Their tents and shanties and more permanent adobes had the newly awakened town growing by leaps and bounds.

The new atmosphere of rush and riches was a sharp spur to Dick's ambitions. He had already discussed the possibility of going into trade with St. Vrain, George Bent, and other merchants and received strong encouragement. His latest trapping and Indian trading ventures had supplied him with considerable capital, while his credit was virtually unlimited.

But there was another and even more immediate reason for starting his new enterprise quickly. Among the newcomers on the Taos business scene was Manuel Le Fevre, a French-Canadian who had come out from St. Louis in the early days and gained a wide reputation as a mountain trader. Dick had known and liked Le Fevre for many years. Now for the first time he met the trader's family and a new element entered their relationship.

Manuel, he discovered with a shock, had a lovely, dark-eyed daughter named Marie. The more Dick saw of her, the less his bachelor independence appealed to him as a permanent way of life. Still he might have let things drift, but half the men in Taos were beating a path to Marie's door. In Dick's nature, rivalry had always been a spur to action.

His marriage to Marie Le Fevre and the opening of Wootton's Trading Post were gala events that drew a host of his old comrades back from distant trails. To his long-time friends he insisted solemnly: "My wandering days are over, boys. No more freezing and sweating and risking my scalp in the wilderness. From now on I'm settling down right here to build my business and raise a family." For a few blissful months he almost made himself believe it.

Most of his former companions withheld comment but Matt Curdy laughed openly and loudly. "I don't know who you think you're foolin', hoss, but it ain't none of us that knows you. You can't no more settle down by the stove than you kin flap them big hands o' yourn and fly."

When he felt restlessness setting in, Dick mounted his pony and rode out for a day or two of hunting, or found an excuse to make business trips to Santa Fe or up to Pueblo and Bent's Fort. It was on one of the latter trips that he discovered a new grave in the little burial plot outside the gate. After a lingering and wasting illness, George Bent had died of consumption at the age of thirty-three.

Of the famous brothers, now only William was left to manage

Bent's Fort and provide half of the Bent & St. Vrain partnership. The trade went on but some vital spark seemed to have gone out of it. William spent more and more time with his wife's people in the Cheyenne village and St. Vrain talked of selling Bent's Fort to the War Department for an army post. Dick rode home with a heavy heart and a feeling of sadness that went beyond the loss of a close friend. It seemed somehow as if a whole world that had been his life was also buried in that grave under the protecting cactus.

Early fall brought a brief flurry of the old excitement. The darkly handsome, much-publicized young army explorer, John Charles Frémont, stopped off at Taos on his way to discover an all-year route over the mountains and the Continental Divide. In St. Louis a group of wealthy businessmen were talking of a transcontinental railroad to link the East with the Far West.

Frémont had an escort of thirty-three men and a hundred pack mules loaded with supplies and surveying instruments. He badly needed an experienced guide and scout and Dick was a logical choice. The wages of one hundred dollars a month were fabulous, the promise of adventure a powerful lure, but Dick had to refuse. Much as he longed to go, he was firmly tied to a booming business and a wife who was expecting his first child. Old Bill Williams—crazy as a coot, they said, but knowing the mountains better than any other man alive—took the job instead. Dick rode with the expedition a few miles out toward the mountains and then turned sadly back. For the first time he understood what was meant by the expression "bonds of matrimony." Those same bonds probably saved Dick's life.

In December, Frémont ignored Bill Williams' advice and warnings and attempted to cross the Uncompahgre Mountains. At twelve thousand feet they were trapped in a savage storm. Eleven men and all their mules froze or starved to death. Old Bill led the survivors out at last, half-dead and some with frozen limbs that would cripple them for life. All Frémont's maps and notes, together with the costly instruments, had to be abandoned.

In Taos, Dick was feeling a surge of the old restlessness from being penned too long inside walls and roof. One morning he abruptly announced, "I'm riding out toward the mountains for a couple-three days' hunting." Late that afternoon he rode over the crest of a rise and almost upon the survivors of the ill-fated Frémont expedition. They had come that close to Taos before collapsing from hunger, cold, and exhaustion. If Dick had not stumbled upon them, it is doubtful if any would have survived.

He gave them what food and robes he had, built up a roaring fire, and raced back to Taos for horses and help. By morning the men were being cared for in homes around the town. Dick took Bill Williams into his own house. Kit Carson, who had moved to Taos, took Frémont in.

Old Bill, whose temper had never been mild, was in a towering rage at Frémont. "The big-mouth, show-offy idjit! He kilt them poor fellers back there as sure as if he'd shot 'em dead, and he'd have kilt the rest of us as well if you hadn't come on us, Dick. I told him and *told* him he'd never get acrosst his way, but he thought he knowed more about mountain winters than old Bill, who's been fightin' 'em for fifty year. I don't hope he dies. I jest hope his arms and legs was so bad froze they drop off."

Frémont was never a man to confess a mistake or accept defeat. As he regained his strength he began planning to start at once on a new route to California. Kit Carson flatly refused to guide the party and Bill Williams would not even speak to him. Dick had his business and his coming family as an excuse.

"Then there's one job you can do for me," Frémont told him, "and I'll pay generously for it. My papers and instruments we had to cache up above the headwaters of the Arkansas are priceless to me. If you'll go up and retrieve them when the snow has gone in the spring, I'll pay you well. You won't have to be away from home more than a few days."

Dick had to refuse Frémont because of other commitments.

Frémont finally set out again, having recruited three veteran mountain men and most of a new escort. Those who had refused to join again came to Dick a few days later. "We're laying claim to the instruments and saddles and other stuff Frémont left up there. We figure we've got pay and damages due us and we mean to collect. If you want to go with us, we'll cut you in for a share. Old Bill's going to guide us to the stuff."

Again Dick was sorely tempted but the small return promised for the effort was not worth risking business and Marie's displeasure. He refused, and again his new ties saved his life. On the way back the party was ambushed by Utes and everyone, including old Bill Williams, was killed.

Dick's sadness at the death of an old friend was somewhat tempered by the birth of his son, who was christened Richens Lacy Wootton, Jr. On the heels of that earthshaking event, he won a rich contract to supply the beef for the army post at Taos. To meet the demand, he had to lead a crew of herders over several hundred miles of country, buying up a few head here and there. He also took over a large tract of land where Huerfano Creek joins the Arkansas east of Pueblo and started his own cattle ranch. The traveling and varied outlets for his energies soothed his restlessness. The Utes, on a new warpath, raided his ranch and trail herds often enough to stave off boredom.

Between chasing Utes and rounding up cattle he had managed to enjoy his family, build up his business, and still find time to scout for the army on a number of hard and dangerous campaigns against Utes, Comanches, Apaches, and Kiowas. He guided the troops that smashed the Navajo uprising, then acted as mediator and interpreter at the signing of the peace settlement.

He had literally dozens of narrow escapes but the fantastic Wootton luck still rode his broad shoulders. In all his years of perilous adventure in the West, he had yet to suffer even a minor flesh wound in any conflict.

He awoke one morning to find his golden empire tumbling around his ears. The Treaty of Guadalupe-Hidalgo had brought an end to the Mexican War and with it an end to the wartime prosperity of Taos. The huge army base was cut back to the role of minor frontier outpost, garrisoned by a handful of regulars. The regiments of rowdy, free-spending volunteers were disbanded and sent home. With them went the insatiable market for flour, beef, sugar, coffee, whiskey, and tobacco, the steady demand for horses, mules, hay, hides, and all the other needs and wants of any army. Dick's profitable beef contract was one of hundreds canceled without notice.

Scores of latecomers simply closed their businesses, abandoned their property, and left for other fields. Dick looked at his huge investment in stock and at his comfortable home and decided to stay and ride out the crisis. He was convinced that sooner or later prosperity would return to a town as advantageously situated as Taos. Meanwhile, there was a trickle of trade from permanent settlers in the valley and an increasing number of travelers. There were even a few brigades of die-hard trappers still going into the mountains.

He used every device to keep his trade and his new ranch going. With hard money scarce in the postwar depression that gripped the country, he went back to the barter system. He took odd jobs, tried prospecting, and even combed the mountains in a fruitless hunt for some of the legendary lost Spanish mines. He led one of the few trading expeditions ever to deal with the treacherous Comanches. While he cleared a good profit, it was a gamble so perilous that he swore never to repeat it.

But while Dick carried on his struggle for survival, a familiar world came to an end in smoke and flame and the crash of exploding gunpowder. With a deep and sickening shock he learned that Bent's Fort was no more.

The death of his last brother had taken the heart out of William Bent. There had been other blows to his spirit. The fur trade that had been his real love was almost dead. He and St. Vrain were quarreling. A terrible cholera epidemic wiped out half the southern Cheyennes in a matter of days. Young Marcellin St. Vrain accidentally killed an Indian and had to flee for his life to St. Louis. Once friendly tribes turned ugly and menaced the fort.

The blows piled up until they became more than William could bear. One day he stripped the great fort of its valuables and sent the employees to camp in the big timbers. Then, alone with his memories, he rolled kegs of gunpowder into the rooms, piled dry wood around, and threw in blazing torches. A column of oily smoke was already rising when William Bent mounted his horse and rode out into the gathering dusk.

Miles to the west, at the mouth of Timpas Creek, a trading caravan making night camp saw half the sky suddenly lit by a lurid glare. Then the deep rolling *boom* of the blast reached their ears and the ground trembled under their feet.

They thought the world had come to an end—and in a sense, they were right.

23

Tʜᴇ news of gold in California swept the country like wild-fire. In New Mexico Territory as elsewhere, more than half the able-bodied men assembled outfits and set out for the goldfields. They poured through Taos by the thousands, pausing only to purchase equipment and supplies for their long journey.

Dick's trade boomed as never before and his beef ranch on the Arkansas became his private gold mine. Within a year he was widely known as the cattle king of the Southwest. His immense herds and the methods he developed for handling them were forerunners of the great cattle empires of the West.

The lure of the gold rush stirred his blood but he was far too busy and too tied down to join the great adventure. His big stock was dwindling rapidly and there were demands for a great many new items that he had never carried. In the spring of 1851 he made a trip back to St. Louis to lay in a new and expanded stock of goods. For speed he decided to travel by horseback as far as Kansas City and take a river steamer from there. A party of men he knew were making the same journey so he joined them. One of the party was Major William Grier who had employed Dick as scout and guide for his campaign against the Utes. A veteran cavalry officer, Grier considered his horsemanship equal to that of any man in the country. He was highly annoyed when Dick betrayed some doubts.

Climbing out of the valley of Taos toward Sangre de Cristo Pass the major set what he considered a proper pace. Dick endured it for a while but he was in a hurry and his patience at last wore thin.

"Can't we travel a mite faster? I figure to get to St. Louis and back this year, but I'll never do it at this pace."

"You'll never get there any faster by wearing out yourself and your horse," Grier said, with a touch of stiffness. "This is the pace best suited for making fast time."

"Maybe in the army, Major," Dick said. "But it sure won't hold up against the kind of hurrying I'm used to."

"Dick," Grier snapped, "I believe my command qualifies me to judge horses and riders. When I say no man can make better time on a long journey than we will, I speak with authority."

"You go right ahead and speak, Major," Dick said, "but if you don't object, I'll just push along my own way. And I've got a hundred dollars here that says I'll be in St. Louis before you fellows get to Kansas City."

"I'll take that," Grier snapped.

"Leave my money with the stable keeper," Dick shouted over his shoulder as he dug heels into his horse's flanks.

Traveling alone across the Plains and constantly alert for hostile Indians, Dick covered the seven hundred miles to Kansas City in a little over seven days. When he picked up his winnings on the return journey, he learned from the liveryman that Major Grier and his companions had stumbled in almost two weeks behind him. Never again did that officer challenge a mountain man to a test of speed and endurance.

Back in Taos, Dick began hearing reports from the California goldfields. Great strikes had been made and enormous fortunes accumulated, but up in the mother lode country there was a desperate shortage of food. Fresh meat, particularly beef and mutton, was so scarce that the little brought in commanded fantastic prices. A sheep, he was told, would easily bring ten times its price in New Mexico.

Dick could turn his back on the uncertainties of prospecting for gold. But here was a certainty whose lure was irresistible. His fertile mind churned over the reports and came up with an incredible plan. He would buy a flock of sheep at New Mexico's low price and drive it across some sixteen hundred miles of barren desert and trackless mountains to the goldfields. His shocked friends called the idea insane and impossible, which was all the spur his stubborn nature needed.

He bought nine thousand sheep, an experienced sheep dog, eight trained lead goats, and a string of pack mules. Another thousand dollars went into supplies, including a generous stock of presents with which he hoped to buy off hostile Indians.

His first major headache came when he tried to round up a crew. Mexican herders were no problem and he engaged fourteen of the best. Rounding up a dependable armed escort proved to be a different matter. Not one of the old companions he knew and trusted was available. Dan Wyler had been killed by Snakes in Wyoming. Matt Curdy and most of the others had gone off to the gold rush.

In the end Dick had to settle for eight shiftless former soldiers of dubious abilities and even more dubious courage. He issued every man a rifle, pistol, and knife and hoped for the best, but he had few illusions. For the first time in his life he was starting on a perilous venture without the backing of men of his own breed and the knowledge was not comforting.

They set out at dawn June 24, 1852. From the start the sheep proved surprisingly tractable, following the lead goats and needing only the dog behind to nip at stragglers. The herders had little to do but gossip in liquid Spanish and roll innumerable corn-shuck *cigarillos*.

In most other ways, the trip was a nightmare. Dick's planned route led up the Rio Grande to its headwaters, then west over the Divide, following easy trails he knew from his trapping expeditions. But he had not reckoned with a late spring snowstorm whose runoff had turned every stream into a roaring torrent, with crossings slow and treacherous.

Near the Uncompahgre River they entered the country of the mountain Utes. Dick had a plan based on his trading experience. When Indians appeared, he would give generous presents and arrange a parley with their head chief to work out satisfactory payment for safe passage across their land. The only trouble was that the Utes refused to appear.

For two days they traveled through hostile country without seeing an Indian. Dick's sharp eyes noted plenty of fresh sign but he kept his forebodings to himself for fear of panicking his nervous crew. At night he had the stock bunched close to a big fire, with guards patrolling in four-hour shifts.

He expected trouble and it came on the third night. A sentry literally fell over Indians creeping up to stampede the flock and his startled yell aroused the camp. The Utes fled while the jittery crew blazed away at empty shadows.

When order had been restored Dick told them grimly, "We'll meet them face to face tomorrow. They've had their try at running off the stock now, and they know we're on guard. They'll be showing up with some new thieving scheme next."

His dark prophecy came true about noon the next day when a war party of over a hundred Utes appeared, blocking the trail. They were in an ugly mood, sitting with drawn bows and cocked guns. With supreme insolence the chief sat with his warriors and forced Dick to ride to him for parley.

"The white man is trespassing on the Indians' land," he began harshly, ignoring Dick's friendship sign. "His animals with the white hair and the stink have destroyed the grass so the Indians' ponies will starve. The white man must pay the Indian for using his ground and destroying his grass before he goes another step. Chief Uncotash has spoken."

Ignoring the threat and the insolence, Dick drew on his best command of signs and the Ute tongue to answer carefully, "Cut-Hand brought many fine presents and useful goods to pay the great Chief Uncotash for his grass and for crossing his land, but Chief Uncotash did not come to receive them. This is not a good place to hold the sheep while we talk. Ahead, by the river, is a place to camp. We will go there and smoke together and enjoy sweet coffee while we agree what is to be paid."

"The white man speaks to the Indian with two tongues. How does Uncotash know Cut-Hand will come there and keep his word?"

"That's easy," Dick said. "I will send some of my men to wait with you until we arrive." He turned in the saddle and indicated three of his escort. "Benson, Leger, Groffault! You ride ahead with Chief Uncotash, pick a campsite by the river, and wait for us to come up."

The trio moved up with obvious reluctance. After a parley among themselves, the Utes wheeled around and rode off with the men. Dick shouted in Mexican and the flock moved ahead.

They had covered barely a mile when the three came streaking back, white-faced and shaking. Benson blurted, "They was set to kill us, I know. We don't savvy their gobble like you do, but the way they looked at us was plain murder, so the first chance we got, we cut and run for it."

"You stupid fools," Dick raged. "Thanks to you, we're in real trouble now. Uncotash will figure this is some kind of a trick to cheat him. . . ."

He broke off as the Utes reappeared at a dead run. As they neared the group, the Indians separated to cut off each of the men. Uncotash and a half dozen warriors closed in around Dick, their weapons ready and hot anger in their eyes. The chief's guttural voice lashed at him in a furious tirade.

"The white man's words are lies. His promises are tricks to cheat and rob the Indian. He never meant to bring presents and make payment by the river."

Dick tried to explain and soothe the savage tempers, but Uncotash shouted him down. He was plainly working himself up to ordering an attack. Dick could feel cold sweat on his back. His men were cut off, surrounded and too terrified to resist. Their only hope lay in a desperate gamble.

Without warning Dick threw himself sideways out of his saddle. One arm swept out to encircle a savage neck as the momentum of his dive hurled Uncotash off his pony. They landed heavily with Dick on top, his solid two hundred pounds smashing the breath from the chief's lungs. Instantly Dick's knife was out, its point against the savage throat.

The nearer Indians were too stunned to move. On the other side of the flock, some Utes saw the sudden movement and began loosing arrows at the sheep. Dick snarled, "Make them stop if you want to go on living."

Uncotash felt death at his throat and shouted a command. The shooting stopped. At Dick's order the Utes pulled back into a sullen group and lowered their weapons. He jumped up then and pulled Uncotash to his feet, keeping the point of his knife hard against the bronze flesh.

"Tell them to go ahead of us to the river. And tell them if they try one tricky move, you're a dead chief." His raised voice lashed at his own frightened crew. "Don't just stand there shaking, you gutless worms! Get those sheep moving."

With Dick and his chastened captive marching ahead, they covered the two miles to the Uncompahgre without incident and made camp. He kept a sharp watch but his prompt action had taken away any Ute desire for trouble. Over cups of sweet coffee, Uncotash readily accepted a modest payment and agreed to leave a hostage as a guarantee against a night attack. Dick was so relieved that he impulsively added a fat bonus of flour and gunpowder to the tribute he handed over.

When, further along, another band of Utes showed evidence of hostility, Dick struck first. He seized one of their number as a hostage for safe passage. Thereafter, he had no further Indian trouble, although their exorbitant demands for tribute so depleted his stock that they had to turn off to Salt Lake City to replenish supplies.

While there, Dick was approached by a well-dressed, gray-haired man who showed great interest in the sheep and particularly in the long trek over the mountains. After talking for some time, Dick thought to introduce himself. He held out his hand. "My name, by the way, is Dick Wootton."

The stranger pumped the hand warmly. "Even out here I've heard of you, Mr. Wootton. My name is Brigham Young, and I'd deem it an honor if you would have supper with me at my home."

Dick accepted, half expecting to find the home of the Mormon leader an exotic harem swarming with wives. He saw only a plain, gaunt woman who served the meal and he spent an enjoyable evening. Dick left with assurances of warm friendship and an invitation to come back at any time.

At Salt Lake City seven of his ex-soldiers and several Mexican herders deserted. Dick managed to hire six drifters even less prepossessing than the original crew and go on, shorthanded. Because of Indian raids and massacres to the west, he decided to stick close to the well-traveled Emigrant Trail. This required a looping course of endless detours to find grass for the sheep, adding two miles of side travel to every mile of forward progress.

His new helpers were sullen and bad-tempered from the beginning. Dick took to waking up every few minutes through the night to make sure the sheep were being guarded, or that his escort had not made off with the mules and supplies. A large band of Indians had been following them for days and the danger of night attack added to Dick's tension.

After a few days he began falling asleep in the saddle and almost toppling to the ground. One morning he told the men, "I'm scouting ahead, but when I'm finished I won't ride back as usual. Do you see those big rocks standing up a few miles ahead? You'll get up to them around noon and you'll find me holed up at the base somewhere, catching some sleep. Burns, I'll delegate you to wake me up as you pass."

His scouting done, Dick found a shaded niche, tethered his riding mule close, and fell sound asleep. He awoke suddenly with a sharp sense of something wrong. Jumping up, he saw the sun low in the afternoon sky. The sheep were nowhere in sight but a clear trail showed where they had made a wide detour past the rocks some hours before.

Dusk was settling in when Dick caught up with the plodding

flock. The men stared with veiled looks as he flung himself out of the saddle. "What's the idea of passing me by? Burns, you had strict orders to wake me when you reached the rocks."

"Oh, was it them rocks back *there* you meant?" Burns said with bland innocence. "I thought you meant some others further ahead, boss."

Dick controlled his temper and let the matter drop, but that night he tucked another pistol into his belt and slept less than ever. The next morning, on sudden impulse he ended his usual scout with a wide circle that brought him onto the trail some distance behind the flock.

The first thing he saw was a band of twenty sheep, left behind and placidly grazing beside the trail. With some difficulty he got them bunched and started toward the main flock. Denger, the one man of his original crew who had not deserted, saw him coming and rode back to help haze the woollies into the flock.

He rode up beside Dick. "You've been square with me and I hate to see you robbed blind. I reckon you don't know what's goin' on. You know the big emigrant train that's been a couple miles behind us all the way from Salt Lake City? Well, those new fellers made a deal with 'em to leave bunches of sheep behind for them to pick up. When they've dropped off enough to pay their passage, they all get to ride the train to Californy."

"I'm much obliged, Tom," Dick said grimly. "Say nothing and I'll handle it."

He waited until night, when the six had laid aside their weapons and were eating supper by the fire, then quietly collected all the guns. Their first inkling of trouble came when Dick stepped into the firelight and covered them with his cocked rifle.

"On your feet, you skunks! I've had all your thieving and scheming I aim to take. Since you're so all-fired anxious to join the train behind us, you can leave right now. Pick up your gear and start walking."

The six were on their feet, gaping at him. Burns blurted,

"You can't send us out there at night without even a pistol to protect ourselves. There are Injuns out there somewhere close."

"The same Indians you were hoping would kill me in my sleep yesterday," Dick snarled. "If you run into them, give 'em my regards. Now start walking and don't look back."

He followed them for some distance back along the trail, ready to shoot at the first sign of trouble, but the toughs were too cowed and frightened to resist. They stumbled off into the darkness and he never saw or heard of them again.

With only Denger and the Mexicans to help, he got over the Sierra Nevadas a jump ahead of the heavy snow. On October 9, just one hundred and seven days out of Taos, he drove his flock into camp outside Sacramento, California. A head count revealed that he had lost only one hundred head on the hazardous trek, including those butchered for food.

Dick wintered in California and rode home in the spring with nearly forty-five thousand dollars in gold and bank drafts in his saddlebags to show for his daring gamble. He made the trip in thirty-three days and arrived to find Marie had presented him with a second daughter, bringing his children to three.

24

Part of Dick's sheep profits went into his booming cattle ranch. Where the rivers met he built a fine log house in the form of a stout fort, with high bastions and a strong stockade. A close friend and sometime partner in business ventures, Joe Doyle, built a smaller house only a hundred yards up the river.

Meanwhile the Utes and Apaches had stepped up their raids to new heights of fury and Dick rarely made the trip back and forth without at least one narrow escape. On one occasion he was chased by a band of Apaches determined to have his scalp and covered the one hundred and sixty-five miles to Taos in a little under twenty-four hours.

The raids grew so fierce that it was not until July 1854 that he dared move his family to the new ranch home, and then only with a strong escort of cavalry from Fort Garland. Once at the fortified ranch, however, with his large crew of tough and self-reliant cowhands, Dick felt they were as safe as anywhere in the West. Within a few months, that belief was badly shaken.

Summer and fall passed quietly. In December, Doyle left his family at Dick's fort and went off on a trading trip to the Arapahos. A few days later three of Dick's friends rode in with a guest. He was John McDougall from New York, on his way to California where his brother James had recently become the state's first attorney general.

"John, here," they told Dick, "has been dyin' to try his hand at hunting. Why not come along and show him the tricks?"

"I reckon it's safe enough," Dick agreed. "We haven't seen hide nor hair of Indians around here in months."

They rode west, up the Arkansas, with Dick jovially promising McDougall two fine buck deer so he could have the antlers as souvenirs. The second morning Dick rode out alone and came upon the tracks of a band of elk. He rode closer and suddenly felt a coldness down his spine that was not from the wind.

The tracks showed the elk had been fleeing, and mingled with the hoofmarks in the fresh snow were the clear tracks of Ute moccasins and pony hoofs. Dick whirled his horse and raced back to the hunters' camp.

"You better pack up fast," he finished, after describing his discovery. "If there's a party of Utes in the vicinity, this is no place for us. Those tracks weren't a day old."

His companions laughed off his alarm. "Don't tell me an old Injun hunter like you is scared of a few mangy Utes."

"You're blame right I'm scared," Dick said grimly. "I've had too many close calls from Utes not to be. Besides, I've got two families and a big ranch to look out for. I'm leaving."

"How about my deer?" McDougall demanded. "You promised absolutely to get me two bucks."

Dick considered the situation for a moment. "All right. I'll make a dicker with you. If I can get you your deer today, will you agree to leave with me first thing in the morning?"

They accepted and Dick set off to keep his part of the bargain. Once more his habitual caution saved his life. He was carefully studying an open slope before venturing onto it when his sharp eye caught sight of Indians. He slipped back to his horse and got away without being seen. On the way back to camp he stumbled upon two fine deer and risked shooting them to satisfy McDougall.

At three in the morning they broke camp and headed back to strike the river at Pueblo. At the fort they found seventeen men, women, and children, badly frightened. An old Mexican had discovered fresh tracks where a band of a hundred or more Indians had crossed the river in the night.

"They were Utes," Dick told them. "Keep the fort gate shut and barred until you know they've left the country."

He and his companions, now thoroughly alarmed, raced down the river, stopping only to warn settlers along the way. They reached the ranch late Christmas Eve and found everything quiet. Nevertheless, Dick spent Christmas forted up and standing watch from the roof of his house. The traders he had warned on the way came by, heading for the safety of the lower river, and urged him to join them. Dick refused, determined to defend his home and property at all costs.

His own ranch crew had gone to Taos to celebrate Christmas, leaving only Dick and his four companions to garrison the fort. He stationed two in each bastion with ample arms and ammunition and resumed his post on the roof.

In midafternoon a rider came pounding to the gate, haggard and exhausted. "I just seen a massacre," he gasped. "I was riding into the fort at Pueblo when I suddenly see it's full of Utes. They was so busy killing and scalping everybody inside that I got off without their seeing me."

"Then it's only a matter of time until they hit us," Dick said. "Come in and help yourself to some guns."

He had little fear that the Indians could get into his stockade. But he looked down the river to where a herd of fine, fat beef was grazing and a lump came into his throat. In the past year some bad investments and an embezzling employee had cost him a great deal of money. The loss of his cattle now would virtually wipe him out.

The day and night passed without alarm. In the morning nine wagons driven by Cherokee Indian teamsters came by, heading upriver. The traders who had fled at Dick's warning had decided it was safe to send their wagons back for goods they had left behind. Even Dick had begun to think the Utes might have turned back after the Pueblo massacre.

The wagons were hardly out of sight when he heard the rattle of heavy gunfire up the river. The firing soon stopped and nine columns of smoke from the burning wagons rose above the trees. He was watching this grimly when he heard the pounding of hoofs from downriver and a dozen armed horsemen raced to his gate. They were settlers from scattered cabins down the Arkansas, come to unite in defending the strongest post.

An hour later from his post on the roof Dick saw the Indians at last. A band of perhaps sixty Utes came into sight and separated into two parties. One group disappeared while the other circled wide around the ranch, heading down toward his herd of cattle.

Dick looked down into the yard, where the horses of the new arrivals still waited to be unsaddled. A glint came into his eye and he went scrambling down.

"The Utes figure we'll stay forted up here and not fight unless they attack the house. How many are game to ride out behind me and teach the varmints that we can fight in the open as well as behind walls?"

A chorus of shouts went up and the whole group went racing out. Dick leaped into the nearest saddle and the little band streamed out in a whooping charge. The unexpected attack took the Utes by complete surprise. When rifles began to bark, the whole band wheeled and fled back up the river. On the way they ran off a dozen or so of Doyle's cattle but not one of Dick's was lost.

It was the end of the great Ute raid and the last they saw of the savages. That afternoon a huge war party of Arapahoes came racing by. They had heard of the danger threatening their friend Cut-Hand and had come to his rescue and to strike their hated enemies. They caught up with the Utes at Coal Creek and administered a savage whipping that ended the menace for a long time to come. Dick and his friends buried the mutilated bodies of the nine teamsters and the seventeen victims at Pueblo.

A short distance from the fort they stumbled across the body of the eighteenth victim. He had apparently been surprised and killed on his way in. Dick looked at the contorted face, then turned away, feeling a sudden wrench of conflicting emotions.

Never again would the brutal Noah Carse debauch and cheat the Indians.

It was the last time Dick's ranch was ever menaced by Indians. Bands of Cheyennes and Arapahoes came by frequently to visit and trade. Throughout his life, Dick never lost their confidence and friendship. Even in the bloodiest days of the Indian Wars, when their mounting resentment against the white man exploded into fearful violence, Dick's wagon trains and property were never once molested, nor one of his employees menaced.

The year following the Pueblo Massacre was one of the longest and dullest in Dick's life. His ranch was prospering. He dug irrigation ditches and planted vast fields of corn and wheat, and built a water-powered grist mill to grind the grain. The lushness of his harvest and his fame as the first American farmer in Colorado reached as far east as St. Louis.

He had never been so thoroughly bored in his life. Old-timers frequently came by, but their talk of the old wild days of the past only sharpened the monotony of the present. Not even an occasional hunt or Indian trading expedition could lift his spirits.

As an antidote to his restlessness, he and Doyle organized a freighting company to haul between Albuquerque, Fort Union, and Kansas City. They were almost ready to begin operations when Marie suddenly came down with a mysterious ailment and died, leaving Dick with a son and three infant daughters. Marie's parents took the girls to raise. Dick Junior was shipped off to his grandparents in Kentucky to be properly raised and educated.

With nothing to hold him back, Dick plunged into freighting with all his pent-up energies. The business prospered from the start. An average wagon train hauled two hundred thousand pounds of goods, on which Dick's freight charge was eight dollars per hundred pounds. After all expenses, a haul between Fort Union and Kansas City left him with a clear profit of at least ten thousand dollars.

To liven things further, Dick started staging races between

his trains and those of rivals crossing the Plains. Betting on the races became a fad, with men wagering as much as five hundred on a wagon. Dick's trains rarely lost. When a mass uprising of Cheyennes, Arapahoes, and Sioux set the Plains aflame, Dick's were the only trains that could get through Indian country without the danger of being looted and burned.

At the conclusion of the brief, bitter Mormon War, Dick led the first wagon train to Salt Lake City and renewed his old acquaintance with Brigham Young. On the way back he had time to take stock of himself. With a shock he realized that he was forty-two years old and that twenty-two years of wilderness hardship had left him with an ache in his bones and a tiredness of spirit. It was time, he decided, to get out while he could.

Back home, he stunned Doyle with an announcement. "I'm quitting and selling out my half of the business, Joe. If you want to buy me out, name your own terms. I'm going back home to Kentucky to see my folks and my son and rest a while. Maybe some day I'll come back West again. There's a pretty little valley up above Raton Pass that I've always hankered to live in. I may settle there some day."

Doyle bought him out and Dick packed for his journey east. Suddenly, at the moment of departure, an aching nostalgia swept over him, a yearning for one more look at his beloved mountains, for one more friendship pipe with his Indian friends. Despite the mounting savagery of the Indian Wars, he knew the Cheyennes and Arapahoes would welcome him to their fires.

Abruptly he canceled his stage passage, bought a half-dozen wagons and loaded them with trade goods. In October 1858 he set out for the Upper Platte River country where he knew his Indian friends would be on their fall hunt, making meat for the long winter ahead. When he had traded out the last gunflint and musket ball and coffee bean, when he had smoked the last pipe and watched the last ceremonial dance, he would say goodbye forever. His wagons would cut east across the Great Plains to Kansas City and steamboat passage home.

With the nostalgia still on him, he chose the same route he had followed twenty-two years before, on his first trading venture to the Sioux. The wagons would go up Fountain Creek, around the foot of Pikes Peak and northward, skirting the edge of the mountains for the last time.

Somewhere along the first miles of the journey, he made a momentous decision. An old friend and companion, one of the last of the mountain men, Blackfoot John Smith, was up on Cherry Creek somewhere near the South Platte, prospecting for gold. To make his farewell complete, he would hunt up John and spend one last night by the fire, yarning over the old days that would never return.

With that decision, he remembered years later, "All my plans and I suppose the whole course of my afterlife was changed."

25

Dᴵᴄᴋ's wagon train reached Cherry Creek on Christmas Eve, but he did not find Blackfoot John Smith. That colorful and eccentric character had wandered off up the Platte somewhere with his son Jack. What he found instead was a scattering of rude cabins on both sides of the little creek and some five hundred rough, unwashed, wild-eyed miners, the vanguard of the Pikes Peak gold rush.

At the sound of his wagons creaking up the east bank of the stream, men came tumbling out of the cabins to surround the train in a shouting, jostling crush. "Welcome to Denver, friend, the greatest little city in the West. Who be ye, stranger? Where you bound for? What's on them wagons?"

Laughing, Dick shouted back: "The name's Dick Wootton, and I'm bound for Indian villages with a stock of trade goods."

"What kind of goods, Wootton?" a man called.

Dick spread his hands. "About anything a redskin craves, I guess. Shirts, blankets, gunpowder, flour, sugar, coffee . . ."

"Did you hear that?" a man yelled. "He's got flour, sugar, coffee."

A score of voices took up the cry, repeating the words as if they had a quality of magic. A bearded miner pushed forward. "Light down, Wootton, and leave the unloading to us. You don't have to go no further to sell out. Man, we haven't tasted bread nor coffee for nigh on two months. Just name your price."

Before Dick could frame an answer, a horde of men splashed across from the cabins on the west side, shouting: "Hold on there, mister. You don't want to get stuck in that shantytown they call Denver. There ain't no future in it. You come on over to Auraria, what's goin' to be the biggest and richest city in the West in a year or two."

A loud and profane argument boiled up and several fistfights broke out. In the midst of the tumult, men seized the teams and began leading them down to the creek. Dick's protests were lost in the uproar as the wagons lurched and splashed across with the whole crowd trailing along in raucous argument.

At one of the larger cabins, men ran inside and began pitching the owner's possessions out into the snow. Others came rolling barrels. These were upended inside and rough planks laid across to form a rude counter.

"There's your store, Wootton," a man shouted. "It ain't much but it'll do for the moment. Tomorrow you tell us what kind of building you want and we'll start puttin' it up right away."

Another man thrust a paper into his hand. "Here you are, Wootton—a deed to a hundred and sixty acres of the best town property, free and clear. It's Auraria's Christmas present to our first storekeeper."

"Now listen," Dick yelled above the din, waving his arms. "Dammit, listen to me! I don't want to settle down and I don't want to keep store. I'm trading out my goods to the Indians and heading home to Kentucky."

There was a sudden sharp silence. A bearded miner shook his head. "If that don't beat all. Here's a feller would ruther leave his own go hungry on Christmas so's he kin peddle fancy grub to the redskins."

Dick looked at the intent faces, then down at the property deed in his hand. He sighed. "Well, I reckon I can always go back for another load of trade goods later."

With the words he abandoned his dream of returning to Kentucky and settled in as the first merchant in Denver. Almost overnight his first stock was taken at top prices and he rushed the wagons back for a larger selection. Meanwhile the whole community helped put up the Wootton Building, the town's first two-story structure and first to be built of hewn logs, as well as the only one with real glass windows. His home, built nearby, was the first frame house.

In April Dick offered his unused upstairs floor to an ambitious young editor by the name of William Byers who wanted to start a newspaper. In the rival town across the creek, young John Merrick was also starting a paper, and a fierce race developed over which would come out first. Great sums were bet and the towns were in a fever of excitement.

When Dick's roof sprung numerous leaks under the weight of a heavy snowfall, Byers pitched a tent over his typecase and little Washington handpress and worked on. Around ten o'clock on Friday night, April 22, 1859, Byers peeled the first issue of his *Rocky Mountain News* from the press, winner of the contest by twenty minutes. The *Cherry Creek Pioneer,* loser by so narrow a margin, sold out to the *News.* Shortly afterward the towns united to become the city of Denver.

As pioneer merchant and property owner, Dick had a large hand in its growth. He donated the use of his store as town meeting hall and helped organize a Vigilance Committee to bring law and order. Later he took a prominent part in making Colorado a state. He built Denver's first hotel but lost money on it because he could never turn away broken-down prospectors who needed a place to sleep, or a few square meals.

When the threat of Indian raids threw the town into a panic, Dick helped organize a militia. He was appointed its first brigadier general, but to his disappointment the threatened attack never came and he had no chance to do any fighting.

Dick left Denver abruptly in 1862, with a posse on his heels and the specter of jail hanging over him. The cause of his sudden fall from favor was the Civil War.

Born in Virginia and raised on the southern border of Kentucky, Dick was naturally a Confederate sympathizer to the core. He made no effort to hide his sentiments, which made him highly unpopular in a predominantly Northern town. His business fell to a trickle and he received so many threats that he took to carrying a loaded pistol and avoiding dark alleys.

When Confederate Colonel Sibley invaded New Mexico with a force of Texas Rangers, a wave of hysteria swept Denver. A rumor was started that Sibley was on his way to Colorado to seize the rich gold and silver mines for the Confederacy.

At the time, Dick was getting ready to ride down to Taos on a business trip. He was just saddling up when a friend, also a Southerner, slipped into the stable. "You better hit that saddle and light out as fast as you can, Dick. Some durn fool started the story that you've got a Rebel plot going to turn the mines over to Sibley and his Rangers."

"I'll be dogged," Dick said. "Though if I had a notion how to do that, I'd probably have tried. I just never thought of it. But who'd believe such a crazy yarn?"

"Plenty of folks, and they're gettin' up a posse right now to arrest you and either hang you or lock you up for the rest of the war. You better git and git quick."

Dick got, heading south at a gallop. Once or twice he got a glimpse of riders behind him, but if it was the posse, they soon gave up the chase.

Shortly afterward he sold out his properties and shook the red dust of Denver from his boots for good. He felt no regrets. The walls of the fast-growing city were closing in on him anyhow and he was bored to death with the life of a city merchant.

Now he started a big farm on Fountain Creek, nine miles above the ruins of the old Fort Pueblo, abandoned since the massacre of 1854. While his farm was getting started, he put up a trading post and a cabin home near the fort. These were the first two buildings in the present city of Pueblo, Colorado.

The soil was unbelievably rich and his hundreds of acres of corn and wheat were the wonder of the country. In the wartime boom, the army bought everything he could raise at top prices. There in the shadow of the mountains he was free, prosperous, and active. At about this time his parents died and young Dick Junior came home, a stocky, good-looking young fellow with many of his father's sturdy characteristics. He helped on the farm for a time, then became wagon master of a freight outfit operating across the Plains.

The great Indian Wars that burst out through the West gave Dick more than enough danger and excitement. Then, in the spring of 1864, his latest farming venture came to an abrupt and violent end.

All through early May the rain poured down in torrents, day and night, until Fountain Creek and all the neighboring streams were roaring over their banks. In the early morning hours of May 12 a cloudburst struck the north flank of Pikes Peak, where Fountain Creek begins.

As usual, Dick was up at daybreak and out in the rain, gloomily looking out across his drowned fields. Suddenly he heard a heavy, rising roar from the north. A moment later a great wall of black water burst into sight, rushing down in flood with the speed of an express train. Later, Dick measured the high-water marks on surviving trees and found the wave to have been eighteen and a half feet high.

With his ingrained caution, Dick had built his house on a high knoll as a safeguard against floods. He yelled and ran for it with the speed of desperation, the noise of the onrushing flood a deafening thunder in his ears.

He made it with only inches to spare as the crest roared by, actually washing over his doorstep but not quite coming inside the house. Other houses down the creek on lower ground were smashed and scattered. His nearest neighbor, a man named Dodson, got his family out only moments before his house was swept away with all their possessions and eleven hundred dollars in gold. Great cottonwoods with trunks five feet in diameter were uprooted by the torrent and hurled with shattering force into other homes down the stream. Nine lives were lost and all property in the valley except Dick's was destroyed.

When the flood subsided, Dick found his fields buried under masses of uprooted trees, plows, farm wagons, and the wreckage of houses and barns. It was a sickening sight, but rooting under the debris and mud Dick discovered that his young corn and wheat had not been completely destroyed.

He raced out to hire all the help he could find and set them to clearing away the rubble. In a few days a sickly sun shone down on fields once more green with young corn and grain. By another week he could safely estimate that better than half his crops had survived.

"I won't get rich this year," he said, "but at least I'll get my costs out and maybe a few dollars' profit for the work."

That afternoon a furious hailstorm struck. Hailstones, many as large as baseballs, shattered windows and roofs, killed or injured much livestock, and smashed Dick's young crops to a hopeless shambles. Not enough survived to be worth cultivating. Dick packed his possessions and turned his back on farming forever.

A new scheme was already hatching in his mind. It was to be one of the most gigantic and sensational enterprises the West had ever seen.

·

26

Dɪᴄᴋ had never forgotten the idyllic little valley he had found high above Raton Pass, nor had he forgotten the Pass itself. Lying across the Colorado-New Mexico line, it offered a short, direct passage between busy Albuquerque and Santa Fe to the south, and fast-growing Trinidad at its northern end. Its use could save days of travel between the East and the booming West.

The difficulty was that Raton Pass was a narrow, tortuous canyon, cut up by swift mountain streams, blocked by huge fallen rocks, and constantly menaced by landslides. The rough, winding trail was hard enough for horsemen and packtrains. Occasionally a small wagon struggled through in summer, but for most of the year it was practically impassable. In 1858 Dick had spent almost a month getting a train of light wagons through on his way to Denver.

Now Dick rode down and picked his way through the Pass, his sharp eyes noting details on every hand. On the way, he climbed seven thousand feet for another look at his beloved valley, no more than a pocket of lush green, almost circled by towering peaks and watered by a swift mountain brook.

Below the south end of the Pass, on Little Cimarron Creek, stood the great ranch of Lucian Maxwell, one of the best known of the mountain men and a long-time acquaintance of Dick's. By varied and devious means, Maxwell had acquired one of the enormous old Spanish land grants that included the whole of Raton Pass in its more than a million acres.

Sitting on the wide veranda of Maxwell's two-story adobe ranch house, Dick said, "Luce, I'd like to buy Raton Pass."

"The Pass?" Maxwell said, startled. "What on earth for, hoss? You can't farm it and there's nothing there worth mining. If it's the hunting you've got in mind, it's not much good any more and you're welcome to do that all you want to anyhow."

"I want to clear it out and make an all-year wagon and stage-coach road," Dick said quietly. "Then I'll set up toll gates and charge everybody that wants to use it for a shortcut."

For a long moment, Maxwell was too stunned to do more than gape. Eventually he recovered his wits and a deal was concluded. For a surprisingly modest sum, Dick received a deed to twenty-five hundred acres, including the Pass itself and its approaches, from the outskirts of Trinidad south to the Red River, a distance of some twenty-seven miles.

Dick's first move was to build a snug home in his little valley above the Pass. While that was going up, he was in the saddle constantly, rounding up a huge crew of laborers. Work started as early in the spring as possible, with crews starting from both ends to clear and grade a road.

It was a Herculean task. Boulders bigger than houses had to be exploded and the fragments carted away. Hillsides and jutting shoulders had to be cut back, gullies filled, and more than forty bridges built. The whole twenty-seven miles of road had to be widened, leveled, and graded solidly enough to bear the heaviest freight traffic.

The work was finally completed and toll stations with drop gates set up at either end, with crews on duty day and night to collect. Business boomed from the start. Freighters and traders found the short, easy road more than worth its cost and it quickly became an accepted part of the old Santa Fe trail. A rising tide of emigrants used it to shorten their journey west. The army made it the main artery of freight traffic and troop movements to the western posts and forts.

When the busy Santa Fe Stagecoach Line adopted his road,

Dick had to put up a large hotel and dining room, which also prospered steadily. Even with the enormous cost of maintaining the road and keeping it clear of snow in winter, his profits mounted steadily.

Not everyone took kindly to the idea of paying toll. As a rule, people from the East were familiar with toll roads and raised no objections, but the idea was an innovation to the West. Mexicans in particular viewed the idea with dark malevolence. The idea of paying to use a road was totally beyond their comprehension and they considered it a diabolical swindle aimed at their nationals. Whenever he saw dark skins and colorful costumes approaching, he braced himself for a noisy argument.

As he remarked dryly years later, "Some tolls I collected by argument and persuasion, and some by the use of a stout club. But I always collected the toll."

There were two exceptions which he made from the start. Sheriffs and their posses on the trail of outlaws were waved on through without delay. He also wisely exempted all Indians from paying toll. While they never understood the principle of a toll road, they did sense that they were being given some kind of preferred treatment and often brought Dick fine gifts.

He had made peace with the Utes who ranged those mountains and hardly a day passed that a few did not drop in to visit and talk of the old days. In one band that stopped was an older Indian of impressive bearing, whose handsome face struck a faint chord in Dick's memory. He studied the visitor for some time and finally asked, "Haven't I encountered you somewhere else a long time ago? I'm sure I've seen you before."

The Indian smiled. "The eyes of Cut-Hand are sharp and his memory long. Once I sat on my horse beside him with my bow drawn when he sprang suddenly and knocked Chief Uncotash to the ground to save his sheep. Afterward we smoked the pipe together at the Uncompahgre River when tribute was arranged."

After their alliance with the Utes, bands of Cheyennes and Arapahoes came down frequently to visit. All the Indians loved to challenge Dick to shooting matches, bringing finely tanned skins to wager. They always lost, but he could never talk them out of betting.

Once when he tried to give back some skins he had won from a Ute chief, the Indian drew himself up and said with dignity, "A Ute always pays his debts."

Old mountain men companions from the early days came long distances to visit him and yarn about the past, so that he was never lonesome for companionship. Most of their talk concerned the disappearance of game. The buffalo had almost vanished from that part of the country. In his first years in the valley, Dick could shoot deer from his front porch, but they were becoming increasingly scarce, frightened away by the mounting traffic on his toll road.

Lucian Maxwell came frequently to visit and occasionally Kit Carson rode down from his ranch on the Purgatory. The new cattle kings, Charlie Goodnight and John Chisum, became frequent visitors.

Never once did Dick have any Indian trouble in the Pass, but outside their raids were increasing in savagery. One evening the westbound stagecoach pounded in, the horses trembling and covered with foam after outrunning a large war party of Comanches. Stuck in the body of the coach were more than a hundred arrows and arrowheads but the passengers and driver had escaped with only minor scratches.

All around Dick the West he had known so long and done so much to shape was changing with frightening rapidity. After one visit with old friends, he could think of nothing but the good smell and taste of fresh buffalo roasting on a fire. At last he got his horse and set out for one last buffalo hunt and feast. When he returned at last he told his friends, with tears in his eyes, of riding clear into Texas before he found the first buffalo.

The years were passing and he was growing tired of the activity and strain of operating his enterprises. A growing network of steel rails was replacing the old roads and trails, driving away the last of the game. In 1878 Dick sold his right of way through

Raton Pass to the Atchison, Topeka and Santa Fe Railroad Company and retired to his snug little home in the valley above.

He was sixty-two now, and it no longer galled his restless spirit to sit quietly and reflect on a full, rich, satisfying life. He had much to be proud of, and he never had time to be lonely.

Dick Junior came often to visit, bringing his vivacious young wife. Young Richens had been elected to the Colorado legislature and he was becoming widely known as a man of importance.

Then something began to happen, something ugly and frightening as nothing had ever frightened Dick before. In his eyes, that once could spot a hidden Indian a mile away, the shapes of his beloved mountains were growing blurred and shadowy. He had to strain harder and harder to make out the cottonwoods down along Raton Creek. At the far end of his valley, the white trunks of the aspens were no more than a pale haze. One morning he awoke to total darkness. The eyes that had watched a nation come of age were blind, filmed by cataracts. He accepted his fate as he had always accepted adversities, without complaining or growing bitter.

It was young Dick Junior who went into action. He arrived one day from his home in Trinidad, bringing one of the best eye surgeons in the West. An operation was performed then and there on the kitchen table.

Two months later, when the bandages were removed, Dick's sight had been partially restored. He could read his papers, recognize the faces of old friends, and once more enjoy the changing seasons as they painted the mountains with the familiar colors. He could not see quite well enough to use his rifle or go on hunts, but he was content.

He died there, quietly and peacefully in 1893 and was buried in his little green valley. The echoing whistle of a transcontinental train, drifting up from Raton Pass, was his requiem.

Around his final resting place, an eager nation surged westward over trails Dick Wootton had blazed for America's future.

About the Author

J OSEPH MILLARD was born in Minnesota and grew up in the town of Canby, near the South Dakota line. His father was second sheriff of Deuel County, Dakota Territory, so he was indoctrinated at an early age in the history of that rugged country.

The elder Millard owned a large cattle ranch on the Dakota border where Joseph spent many of his early days. He later rode range as a cowhand for the larger ranches of the Sand Hill country of Nebraska.

He stumbled into publishing as advertising manager of regional trade journals in Minneapolis and then discovered he had an interest in writing. His first sale, a piece of fiction about Washington at Valley Forge, was sold to a Sunday School paper for six dollars and since that time he has never ceased to write.

Since 1938 Mr. Millard has been a full-time writer. Among his books are *The Wickedest Man,* a biography of a Pennsylvania oil boom character; *Edgar Cayce,* a biography of a noted mystic; *Civil War Stories From True,* which he edited; *The Cheyenne Wars;* and *The Gods Hate Kansas.*

In 1952 he wrote a short biography of Dick Wootton for *True* magazine. His son, Michael, then 12 years old, blurted out, after reading the article, "Why don't you write a whole book about him and call it *Cut-Hand the Mountain Man?*" Mr. Millard made a vague promise to write it "someday" and through the years Michael has continually needled him about it.

When Michael Millard called him to announce the birth of the first grandson, he said to his father, *"Now* will you write that book so *he* can read it someday?" As the author says in his dedication, Michael "supplied the title and applied the spur."